Workbook for
Providing Home Care
A Textbook for Home Health Aides

FIFTH EDITION

Credits

Managing Editor
Susan Alvare Hedman

Cover Designer
Kirsten Browne

Cover Illustrator
Jo Tronc

Interior Illustrator
Thad Castillo

Production
Thad Castillo

Proofreaders
Kristin Calderon
Joanna Owusu

Copyright Information

© 2017 by Hartman Publishing, Inc.
1313 Iron Ave SW
Albuquerque, New Mexico 87102
(505) 291-1274
web: hartmanonline.com
email: orders@hartmanonline.com
Twitter: @HartmanPub

ISBN 978-1-60425-068-8

PRINTED IN THE USA

Second Printing, 2019

Notice to Readers

Though the guidelines and procedures contained in this text are based on consultations with healthcare professionals, they should not be considered absolute recommendations. The instructor and readers should follow employer, local, state, and federal guidelines concerning healthcare practices. These guidelines change, and it is the reader's responsibility to be aware of these changes and of the policies and procedures of her or his healthcare facility.

The publisher, author, editors, and reviewers cannot accept any responsibility for errors or omissions or for any consequences from application of the information in this book and make no warranty, express or implied, with respect to the contents of the book. The publisher does not warrant or guarantee any of the products described herein or perform any analysis in connection with any of the product information contained herein.

Gender Usage

This workbook uses gender pronouns interchangeably to denote healthcare team members and clients.

Table of Contents

Preface

Welcome to the *Workbook for Providing Home Care: A Textbook for Home Health Aides*! This workbook is designed to help you review what you have learned from reading your textbook. For this reason, the workbook is organized around learning objectives, just like the textbook and even your instructor's teaching material.

These learning objectives work as a built-in study guide. After completing the exercises for each learning objective in the workbook, ask yourself if you can DO what that learning objective describes.

If you can, move on to the next learning objective. If you cannot, just go back to the textbook, reread that learning objective, and try again.

We have provided procedure checklists close to the end of the workbook. The answers to the workbook exercises are in your instructor's teaching guide.

Happy learning!

1

Home Care and the Healthcare System

1. Describe the structure of the healthcare system and describe ways it is changing

Matching

For each of the following terms, write the letter of the correct definition from the list below. Use each letter only once.

1. _____ Facilities

2. _____ HMOs (health maintenance organizations)

3. _____ Managed care

4. _____ Payers

5. _____ PPOs (preferred provider organizations)

6. _____ Providers

(A) Cost-control strategies employed by many health insurance plans

(B) People or organizations that provide health care

(C) Places where health care is delivered or administered

(D) A health plan which states that clients must use a particular doctor or group of doctors

(E) People or organizations paying for health-care services

(F) A network of providers that contract to provide health services to a group of people

Multiple Choice

Circle the letter of the answer that best completes the statement or answers the question.

7. Another name for a long-term care facility is
   (A) Skilled nursing facility
   (B) Home health care agency
   (C) Assisted living facility
   (D) Adult day services facility

8. Assisted living facilities are initially for
   (A) People who need around-the-clock intensive care
   (B) People who need some help with daily care
   (C) People who will die within six months
   (D) People who need to be in an acute care facility

9. Care given by specialists to restore or improve function after an illness or injury is called
   (A) Acute care
   (B) Subacute care
   (C) Rehabilitation
   (D) Hospice care

10. Care given to people who have approximately six months or less to live is called
    (A) Acute care
    (B) Subacute care
    (C) Rehabilitation
    (D) Hospice care

2. Explain Medicare and Medicaid, and list when Medicare recipients may receive home care

True or False
Mark each statement with either a T for true or an F for false.

1. _____ To qualify for home health care, Medicare recipients usually must be unable to leave home.

2. _____ Medicare pays for any care that the recipient desires.

3. _____ Medicare only covers people aged 65 or older.

4. _____ One reason that a person may qualify for Medicaid is that he has a low income.

5. _____ Home health care is not covered by Medicare.

6. _____ Medicare has two parts: hospital care and doctor services.

7. _____ Medicare pays for 100% of all home care costs.

3. Explain the purpose of and need for home health care

Fill in the Blank
Fill in the blanks with the correct word for each of the following statements.

1. Home care is less _____ than a long hospital or extended care facility stay.

2. The growing numbers of _____ people and _____ people are also creating a demand for home care services.

3. One of the most important reasons for health care in the home is that most people who are ill or disabled feel more

_____

at home.

4. List key events in the history of home care services

Multiple Choice

1. What event happened in 1959 that noted the need for home health care?
   (A) Homemakers were ordered to war so they were unable to help out at home.
   (B) A national conference on homemaker services was held.
   (C) The Medicare program was created.
   (D) A national holiday commemorating homemakers was established.

2. When was Medicare created?
   (A) 1912
   (B) 1996
   (C) 1965
   (D) 1959

3. Why has interest in home health care increased in recent years?
   (A) The population of elderly people and people with chronic diseases has grown.
   (B) Many hospitals have closed due to lack of business.
   (C) Healthcare costs have decreased.
   (D) Insurance companies often cover 100% of the costs of home health care.

4. What is the function of a diagnosis-related group (DRG)?
   (A) It pairs people with like illnesses together to form a support system.
   (B) It offers formal training for people with disabilities to reenter the workplace.
   (C) It specifies the treatment cost that Medicare or Medicaid will pay for various diagnoses.
   (D) It provides financial assistance for people with debilitating illnesses.

5. Identify the basic methods of payment for home health services

Short Answer
Answer each of the following in the space provided.

1. Identify five basic methods of payment for home health services.

_____

_____
_____
_____
_____

2. What happens when an agency's cost of providing care for a client exceeds the Medicare payment?

_____
_____
_____
_____

6. Describe a typical home health agency

Labeling
Fill in the four blanks below to complete the organizational chart of a typical home health agency. Some blanks have already been completed.

7. Explain how working for a home health agency is different from working in other types of facilities

Fill in the Blank

1. Home health aides (HHAs) must be aware of personal _____ when traveling alone to visit clients.

2. HHAs may have a lot more contact with clients' _____ in the home than they would in a facility.

3. A supervisor monitors an HHA's work, but the HHA will spend most of her hours working with clients without direct supervision. Thus, she must be independent and

   _____.

4. Careful written and verbal

   _____

   skills are important.

5. HHAs need to be _____ in order to adapt to the changes in the environment.

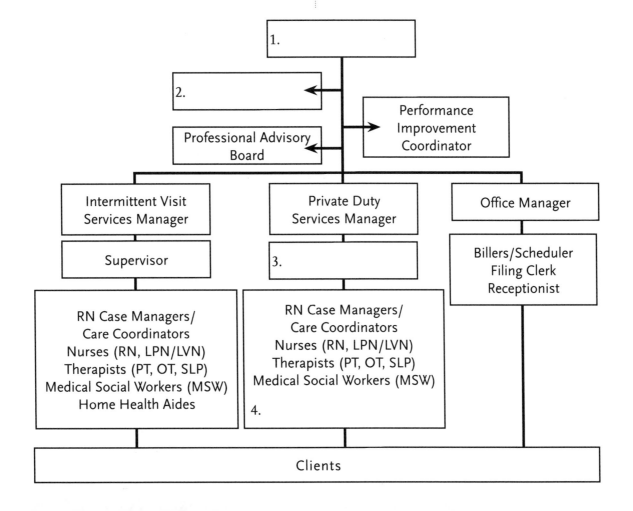

6. In a client's home, the HHA is a
_____ and should
be respectful of the client's property and
customs.

2

The Home Health Aide and the Care Team

1. Identify the role of each care team member

Matching
Use each letter only once.

1. _____ Case Manager or Supervisor

2. _____ Client

3. _____ Home Health Aide (HHA)

4. _____ Medical Social Worker (MSW)

5. _____ Occupational Therapist (OT)

6. _____ Physical Therapist (PT or DPT)

7. _____ Physician or Doctor (MD or DO)

8. _____ Registered Dietitian (RDT)

9. _____ Registered Nurse (RN)

10. _____ Speech-Language Pathologist (SLP)

(A) Develops a treatment plan and administers therapy in an effort to improve the client's physical status and prevent problems

(B) Coordinates, manages, and provides care, as well as supervises HHAs and develops HHA assignments

(C) Diagnoses disease or disability and pre-scribes treatment

(D) Creates and supervises each client's care plan and makes changes to the care plan when necessary

(E) Helps clients get support services, such as counseling and meal services

(F) Performs assigned tasks, such as measuring vital signs, providing personal care, and reporting observations to other care team members

(G) Assesses a client's nutritional status and develops a treatment plan that may include creating special diets

(H) Identifies communication disorders and creates a care plan, as well as teaches exercises to help the client improve or overcome speech impediments

(I) Person whose condition, goals, priorities, treatment, and progress are what the care team revolves around

(J) Helps clients learn to adapt to disabilities by training clients to perform activities of daily living and other activities

2. Describe the role of the home health aide and explain typical tasks performed

Short Answer

1. What are two ways in which home health aides maintain the independence, health, and well-being of clients?

_____

_____

_____

_____

_____

2. List and give examples of two ways in which home health aides provide services to their clients.

_____

_____

_____

Name: _____

_____
_____
_____
_____
_____
_____

3. Identify tasks outside the scope of practice for home health aides

True or False

1. _____ Home health aides never administer medications unless they are trained and assigned to do so.

2. _____ Home health aides are trained to perform invasive procedures.

3. _____ Home health aides should ignore any requests that are outside of their scope of practice.

4. _____ Home health aides must not accept any request that is not part of their job description or that is not on the assignment sheet.

5. _____ The correct way to deal with an unacceptable request is to explain why the request cannot be met, and report it to the supervisor.

6. _____ Home health aides should not perform procedures that require sterile technique.

7. _____ It is acceptable for home health aides to prescribe certain medications if they have permission from their supervisor.

8. _____ Home health aides should only inform the client or family of the diagnosis or medical treatment plan if the client asks.

9. _____ Home health aides may perform any task for which they have been trained, even if it is not part of their assignment.

4. Define the client care plan and explain its purpose

True or False

1. _____ The purpose of the client care plan is to give suggestions for care, which the home health aide can customize for each client.

2. _____ Home health aides should not perform activities that are not listed on the care plan.

5. Describe how each team member contributes to the care plan

Short Answer
List contributions that each of the following care team members might make in developing the care plan.

1. Home Health Aide (HHA)

_____
_____
_____

2. Case Manager or Supervisor

_____
_____
_____
_____

3. Physician (MD or DO)

_____
_____
_____
_____
_____

4. Medical Social Worker (MSW)

_____
_____
_____
_____

_____

_____

6. List the federal regulations that apply to home health aides

Multiple Choice

1. Home health aides must complete at least ____ hours of training before they begin working.
   (A) 30
   (B) 50
   (C) 75
   (D) 100

2. How many hours of annual education (in-service training) must home health aides complete?
   (A) 12
   (B) 62
   (C) 75
   (D) 19

3. What is the name of the federal government agency that makes rules to protect workers from bloodborne pathogens and other hazards while on the job?
   (A) Occupational Safety and Health Administration (OSHA)
   (B) Office of the Attorney General (OAG)
   (C) Environmental Protection Agency (EPA)
   (D) Department of Education (DOE)

7. Describe the purpose of the chain of command

Multiple Choice

1. Which of the following statements is true of the chain of command?
   (A) It describes the line of authority.
   (B) It is the same as the care team.
   (C) It details the process for granting medical licenses to home health aides.
   (D) Home health aides are at the top of the chain of command.

2. Liability is a legal term that means
   (A) The line of authority in an agency
   (B) Ignoring a client's request
   (C) Someone can be held responsible for harming someone else
   (D) A task that a person is not trained for

3. Why should home health aides not do tasks that are not assigned to them?
   (A) The HHA may be assigned more work if he performs additional tasks.
   (B) The HHA may put himself or a client in danger.
   (C) The HHA may need to pay for additional training.
   (D) The HHA may have to arrive at work earlier.

4. What is one reason that other members of the care team will show great interest in the work that a home health aide does?
   (A) They may not trust the HHA.
   (B) The HHA will be working under the authority of others' licenses.
   (C) They may not have much respect for the HHA.
   (D) They can avoid having to pay the HHA if she makes a mistake.

8. Define policies and procedures and explain why they are important

Short Answer
List five examples of common policies and procedures at home health agencies.

1. _____

_____

_____

2. _____

_____

_____

3. _____

_____

_____

Name: _____

4. _____

_____

_____

5. _____

_____

_____

9. List examples of a professional relationship with a client and an employer

Short Answer

Read each of the following scenarios and answer the questions.

1. Kathy, a home health aide, wakes up late and decides to skip her morning shower to make up for lost time. She also skips breakfast because she wants to make her first assignment on time. Because she is feeling so rushed, she forgets to respond when her client says, "Good morning." Instead, she complains to her client about her sleepless night, headache, and lack of breakfast.

    Was Kathy behaving professionally?

    _____

    What should she have done instead?

    _____

    _____

    _____

    _____

    _____

2. At her next client's home, Kathy asks to use the bathroom. She washes her hands carefully when she is finished, and begins to prepare her client's lunch. She listens to her client talk about his grandchildren's visit the day before and encourages her client to share photographs of the grandchildren. As Kathy is leaving, her client offers her a gift. Kathy politely refuses the gift and explains that it is against her agency's policy.

List all the examples of Kathy's professional behavior.

_____

_____

_____

_____

_____

_____

_____

3. Steve, a home health aide, runs out of time at one client's home and is unable to finish his assignment. When his supervisor finds out, she tells him that he needs to work more efficiently. This makes Steve very upset, and he begins to wonder if his job is worth all the criticism he seems to be getting.

    Was Steve behaving professionally?

    _____

    What should he have done instead?

    _____

    _____

    _____

    _____

4. At his next meeting with his supervisor, Steve explains why he was unable to finish his assignment and asks his supervisor for suggestions. She shows him how to organize his time more efficiently. After asking several more questions, Steve feels that he now understands how to work more effectively. Being able to communicate in a positive way with his supervisor improves Steve's attitude about his job.

    List all the examples of Steve's professional behavior.

    _____

    _____

Name: _____

_____
_____
_____
_____
_____

10. Demonstrate how to organize care assignments

Short Answer

1. Why is it important for a home health aide to organize his work?

_____
_____
_____
_____
_____
_____
_____

2. Why should the home health aide include the client in planning his schedule?

_____
_____
_____
_____
_____
_____
_____

11. Demonstrate proper personal grooming habits

Multiple Choice

1. How often should a home health aide bathe?
    (A) Twice per month
    (B) Every day
    (C) Every other day
    (D) Twice per week

2. Which of the following should a home health aide wear to work?
    (A) Dangling earrings
    (B) An identification badge
    (C) After-shave lotion
    (D) Acrylic nails

3. Which of the following is part of proper grooming for a home health aide?
    (A) Long hair that is tied back
    (B) Long, trimmed beards
    (C) Long, clean nails
    (D) Dramatic eye makeup

4. Which of the following would be the best choice for a home health aide to wear to work?
    (A) Unscented lotion
    (B) Floral fragrance
    (C) Eucalyptus oil
    (D) Musk cologne

12. Identify personal qualities a home health aide must have

Matching
Use each letter only once.

1. _____ Compassionate

2. _____ Conscientious

3. _____ Dependable

4. _____ Empathetic

5. _____ Honest

6. _____ Patient

7. _____ Respectful

8. _____ Sympathetic

9. _____ Tactful

10. _____ Tolerant

11. _____ Unprejudiced

(A) Being caring, concerned, considerate, empathetic, and understanding

(B) Giving the same quality of care, regardless of age, gender, sexual orientation, religion, race, ethnicity, or condition

(C) Being guided by a sense of right and wrong

(D) Valuing other people's individuality and treating others politely and kindly

(E) Speaking and acting without offending others

(F) Being truthful

(G) Getting to work on time and doing assigned tasks skillfully

(H) Respecting others' beliefs and practices and not judging others

(I) Identifying with the feelings of others

(J) Sharing in the feelings and difficulties of others

(K) Not losing one's temper easily, not acting irritated or annoyed, not rushing clients

13. Identify an employer's responsibilities

Short Answer
List and describe seven responsibilities of the employer to the home health aide.

1. _____

_____

_____

2. _____

_____

_____

3. _____

_____

_____

4. _____

_____

_____

5. _____

_____

_____

6. _____

_____

_____

_____

7. _____

_____

_____

_____

3

Legal and Ethical Issues

1. Define the terms *ethics* and *laws* and list examples of legal and ethical behavior

Short Answer

1. Sarah, a home health aide, is out shopping with her friends. One of them asks her if she likes her job, and she responds enthusiastically. She proceeds to relate to them that her client, Mrs. Daly, has Alzheimer's disease and has to be reminded of her name several times a day, as she is apt to forget it.

   Did Sarah behave in a legal and ethical manner? Why or why not?

   _____

   _____

   _____

   _____

   _____

   _____

2. Caroyl, a home health aide, finishes her duties for the day early. Her client, Mr. Leach, tells her how pleased he is with her work. He says that she is the first aide that has made him feel so comfortable and well taken care of. He gives her a little box of candy and says it is for all the hard work she has done. Caroyl initially refuses, but after he insists, she takes it from him, thanking him.

   Did Caroyl behave in a legal and ethical manner? Why or why not?

   _____

   _____

   _____

   _____

   _____

   _____

   _____

3. Mark, a home health aide, has been working for Mrs. Hedman for almost a year. Her family is visiting from out of state and Mark meets her daughter, Susan, for the first time. During the course of conversation, Susan asks Mark to come have a drink with her so that they can talk about her mother's case in a more relaxed environment. Mark tells her that he can go out for a short while. They arrange to meet.

   Did Mark behave in a legal and ethical manner? Why or why not?

   _____

   _____

   _____

   _____

   _____

   _____

   _____

   _____

2. Explain clients' rights and discuss why they are important

True or False

1. _____ If a home health aide knows that a client is being abused by a family member, he should immediately confront the abuser.

Legal and Ethical Issues

2. _____ If a home health aide suspects that a client is being abused, he should not report it until he has proof that the abuse is actually happening.

3. _____ Clients have the right to participate in their care planning.

4. _____ Clients should only be informed of obstacles or barriers to their care if they are life-threatening.

5. _____ Neglect is the failure to provide needed care that results in the physical, mental, or emotional harm to a person.

6. _____ Clients do not need to know what they are being charged for, as long as they are receiving adequate care.

Matching
Use each letter only once.

7. _____ Abuse

8. _____ Active neglect

9. _____ Assault

10. _____ Battery

11. _____ Domestic violence

12. _____ False imprisonment

13. _____ Financial abuse

14. _____ Involuntary seclusion

15. _____ Malpractice

16. _____ Neglect

17. _____ Negligence

18. _____ Passive neglect

19. _____ Physical abuse

20. _____ Psychological abuse

21. _____ Sexual abuse

22. _____ Sexual harassment

23. _____ Substance abuse

24. _____ Verbal abuse

25. _____ Workplace violence

(A) Actions or the failure to act or provide the proper care, resulting in unintended injury

(B) The repeated use of legal or illegal drugs, cigarettes, or alcohol in a way that harms oneself or others

(C) Any unwelcome sexual advance or behavior that creates an intimidating, hostile, or offensive working environment

(D) Purposeful failure to provide needed care, resulting in harm to a person

(E) The separation of a person from others against the person's will

(F) The unlawful restraint of someone that affects the person's freedom of movement

(G) Verbal, physical, or sexual abuse of staff by other staff members or clients

(H) Intentionally touching a person without his or her consent

(I) A threat to harm a person, resulting in the person feeling fearful that he or she will be harmed

(J) The improper or illegal use of a person's money, possessions, property, or other assets

(K) The forcing of a person to perform or participate in sexual acts

(L) The use of spoken or written words, pictures, or gestures that threaten, embarrass, or insult a person

(M) Emotional harm caused by threatening, scaring, humiliating, intimidating, isolating, or insulting a person, or by treating him or her as a child

(N) Physical, sexual, or emotional abuse by spouses, intimate partners, or family members

(O) Purposeful mistreatment that causes physical, mental, or emotional pain or injury to someone

(P) Any treatment, intentional or unintentional, that causes harm to a person's body—includes slapping, bruising, cutting, burning, physically restraining, pushing, shoving, and rough handling

(Q) The unintentional failure to provide needed care, resulting in physical, mental, or emotional harm to a person

(R) Injury caused by professional misconduct through negligence, carelessness, or lack of skill

(S) The failure to provide needed care that results in physical, mental, or emotional harm to a person

3. List ways to recognize and report elder abuse and neglect

Short Answer

1. Name ten suspicious injuries that should be reported.

_____

_____

_____

_____

_____

_____

_____

_____

_____

_____

_____

_____

2. What is a mandated reporter?

_____

_____

_____

_____

_____

4. List examples of behavior supporting and promoting clients' rights

Multiple Choice

1. When performing a procedure on a client, the home health aide (HHA) should
   (A) Try to distract the client so he will not know what the HHA is doing
   (B) Explain the procedure fully before performing it
   (C) Wait until the client is reading before starting the procedure
   (D) Notify the physician first

2. Which of the following would be the best response by an HHA if a client refuses to take a bath?
   (A) The HHA should offer the client a prize if she will take the bath.
   (B) The HHA should respect the client's wishes, but report the refusal to the supervisor.
   (C) The HHA should explain that he might lose his job if the client does not take the bath.
   (D) The HHA should explain to the client why it is wrong not to bathe.

3. An HHA's husband asks her to tell him some personal details about one of her clients. The best response by the HHA would be to
   (A) Explain that she cannot talk about the client
   (B) Tell him a story if he promises to keep it confidential
   (C) Make up a story to tell, so as not to share anything private
   (D) Tell him something that the HHA knows that the client would not mind her sharing

4. If an HHA suspects his client is being abused, he should
   (A) Open the client's mail and look through his belongings to find any clues
   (B) Keep watching the client to make sure his suspicions are correct
   (C) Report it to his supervisor immediately
   (D) Check with other home health aides to get some advice

5. Explain HIPAA and list ways to protect clients' confidentiality

Multiple Choice

1. What is the purpose of the Health Insurance Portability and Accountability Act (HIPAA)?
   (A) To monitor quality of care in client's homes
   (B) To protect and secure the privacy of health information
   (C) To reduce incidents of abuse
   (D) To provide health insurance for uninsured elderly people

2. What is included under protected health information (PHI)?
   (A) Patient's favorite food
   (B) Patient's favorite color
   (C) Patient's social security number
   (D) Patient's library card number

3. What is the correct response by an HHA if someone who is not directly involved with a client's care asks for a client's PHI?
   (A) Give them the information
   (B) Ask the client if they may have the information
   (C) Ask them to send a written request for the information
   (D) Tell them that the information is confidential and cannot be shared

4. Which of the following is one way to keep private health information confidential?
   (A) Making comments about clients on Facebook
   (B) Discussing clients' progress with a coworker in a restaurant
   (C) Not leaving detailed information for clients in voicemail messages
   (D) Only discussing clients' conditions with friends or family members

5. The abbreviation for a law that was enacted as a part of the American Recovery and Reinvestment Act of 2009 to expand the protection and security of consumers' electronic health records (EHR) is called
   (A) HISEAL
   (B) HITECH
   (C) HIHELP
   (D) HIQUIET

6. Discuss and give examples of advance directives

Matching

1. _____ Advance directives

2. _____ Living will

3. _____ Durable power of attorney for health care

4. _____ Do-not-resuscitate (DNR) order

(A) A signed, dated, and witnessed legal document that appoints someone else to make the medical decisions for a person in the event he or she becomes unable to do so

(B) Outlines the medical care a person wants, or does not want, in case he or she becomes unable to make those decisions; *directive to physicians* and *medical directive* are other terms used to describe this

(C) Legal documents that allow people to decide what kind of medical care they wish to have if they cannot make those decisions themselves

(D) A legal document that tells medical professionals not to perform CPR (cardiopulmonary resuscitation) if breathing or the heartbeat stops

7. Identify community resources available to help the elderly

Short Answer

1. What is one way an HHA can locate community resources for the elderly?

_____

_____

4

Communication and Cultural Diversity

1. Define communication

Short Answer

1. List the three basic steps of communication.

_____
_____
_____
_____
_____
_____
_____
_____
_____
_____
_____

2. Why is feedback an important part of communication?

_____
_____
_____
_____
_____
_____
_____

3. With whom must home health aides be able to communicate?

_____
_____
_____
_____
_____
_____
_____
_____
_____
_____

2. Explain verbal and nonverbal communication

Multiple Choice

1. Which of the following is an example of nonverbal communication?
   (A) Asking for a glass of water
   (B) Pointing to a glass of water
   (C) Screaming for a glass of water
   (D) Saying, "I do not like water."

2. Verbal communication includes
   (A) Facial expressions
   (B) Nodding one's head
   (C) Speaking
   (D) Shrugging one's shoulders

3. Types of nonverbal communication include
   (A) Speaking
   (B) Facial expressions
   (C) Yelling
   (D) Oral reports

4. Which of the following is an example of a confusing or conflicting message (saying one thing and meaning another)?
(A) Mr. Carter smiles happily and tells his home health aide that he is excited because his daughter is coming to visit.
(B) Mrs. Sanchez looks like she is in pain. When her home health aide asks her about it, Mrs. Sanchez tells her that her back has been bothering her.
(C) Ms. Jones agrees with her home health aide when she says it is a nice day, but Ms. Jones looks angry.
(D) Mr. Lee will not watch his favorite TV show. He says he is a little depressed.

5. In the previous question, how could the home health aide clarify the confusing or conflicting message?
(A) State what the HHA has observed and ask if the observation is correct
(B) Ignore the conflicting message and accept what the client has said
(C) Ask the client to repeat what he or she has just said
(D) Tell the client that the HHA knows he or she is not telling the truth

6. Which of the following is true of cultures?
(A) All cultural groups view standing close to another person as a potential threat.
(B) The use of touch is the same for all cultures.
(C) Each culture may have different behaviors, attitudes, and customs.
(D) Maintaining eye contact while talking is preferred by all cultures.

3. Identify barriers to communication

Crossword
Across

3. Type of terminology that may not be understood by clients or their families; HHAs should speak in simple, everyday words

5. These types of questions should be asked because they elicit more than a "yes" or "no" answer

7. Phrases used over and over again that do not really mean anything

Down

1. This type of language, along with gestures and facial expressions, is part of nonverbal communication; HHAs should be aware of this when speaking

2. Being this way and taking time to listen when clients are difficult to understand help promote better communication

4. HHAs cannot offer opinions or give this because it is not within their scope of practice

6. Asking this should be avoided when clients make statements because it often makes people feel defensive

8. Along with profanity, these type of words and expressions should not be used by HHAs

4. List ways to make communication accurate and complete and explain how to develop effective interpersonal relationships

Multiple Choice

1. One way for an HHA to be a good listener is to
(A) Finish a client's sentences for him to show that the HHA understands what the client is saying
(B) Pretend that the HHA understands what a client is saying even if she does not
(C) Restate the message in the HHA's own words
(D) Fill in any pauses to avoid awkwardness

2. Active listening involves
   (A) Focusing on the sender and giving feedback
   (B) Avoiding speaking to the client if the HHA cannot understand him
   (C) Deciding what the client is going to say before he says it
   (D) Talking about the HHA's personal problems

3. Mrs. Velasco is a new client who recently moved to the United States. Simon, her home health aide, is giving her a bath before helping her into bed. He notices that she seems to have difficulty speaking English and seems nervous. What can Simon do to make her more comfortable?
   (A) Give her advice about how to fit in better with American culture
   (B) Talk constantly so that she will not have to speak
   (C) Use some words and phrases that he is familiar with in her language
   (D) Avoid speaking to her while giving care

4. When clients report symptoms or feelings, the best response by the HHA is to
   (A) Interrupt the client
   (B) Ignore the client
   (C) Avoid speaking
   (D) Ask for more information

5. Which of the following statements reflects a way for an HHA to have positive relationships with clients?
   (A) The HHA should fold her arms in front of her while clients are talking.
   (B) The HHA should tell clients she knows exactly how they feel, so clients will feel that they have something in common.
   (C) The HHA should ignore a client's request if she knows she cannot fulfill it.
   (D) The HHA should be empathetic and try to understand what clients are going through.

6. Mr. Vernon is an elderly client who has terminal cancer. He is telling Katie, his home health aide, that he is very depressed about dying. He feels he has left many things unfinished. Hearing this makes Katie uncomfortable. Which of the following would be the best response by Katie?
   (A) She should ignore what he is saying.
   (B) She should try to interest him in a brighter subject.
   (C) She should listen to him and ask questions when appropriate.
   (D) She should tell him she knows how he feels.

True or False
For each of the following statements, write T if the suggestion will help HHAs develop good relationships with clients, and write F if it will not.

7. ____ The HHA should be empathetic.

8. ____ If a subject makes the HHA feel uncomfortable, she should change the subject.

9. ____ The HHA should lean forward in her chair when listening to clients.

10. ____ The HHA should not talk down to clients.

11. ____ If the HHA cannot honor a particular request, she should just ignore it.

12. ____ The HHA should tell clients that she knows how they feel.

13. ____ The HHA should approach clients who are talking.

5. Describe the difference between facts and opinions

Fact or Opinion
For each statement, decide whether it is an example of a fact or an opinion. Write F for fact or O for opinion in the space provided.

1. ____ It is better to take your bath before you eat.

2. ____ You will get depressed if you stay in your pajamas all day.

3. ____ Mr. Ellington sounds angry.

4. ____ My agency says I cannot accept a gift.

5. ____ Your care plan calls for snacks between meals.

6. ____ Ms. Porter did not drink any of her milk at dinner time.

7. ____ I think Mr. Holling is lonely.

8. ____ Mr. Larking's pulse was elevated last night after dinner, but it was back to normal this morning.

9. ____ Mr. Ford drinks more coffee than is good for him.

10. ____ Mr. Ford drinks three cups of coffee every morning.

11. ____ Mrs. Myers needs assistance to stand up.

12. ____ Mrs. Myers looks like she is in a lot of pain.

6. Describe basic medical terminology and approved abbreviations

Matching
For each of the following abbreviations, write the letter of the correct term from the list below.

1. ____ ac, a.c.
2. ____ amb
3. ____ BM
4. ____ C
5. ____ c/o
6. ____ CPR
7. ____ F
8. ____ ft
9. ____ f/u, F/U
10. ____ hs, HS
11. ____ I&O
12. ____ NPO
13. ____ OOB
14. ____ pc, p.c.
15. ____ prn, PRN
16. ____ PWB
17. ____ ROM
18. ____ SOB

19. ____ vs, VS

20. ____ w/c, W/C

(A) Fahrenheit degree
(B) Hours sleep
(C) After meals
(D) Nothing by mouth
(E) Bowel movement
(F) Cardiopulmonary resuscitation
(G) Complains of
(H) Range of motion
(I) Partial-weight-bearing
(J) Vital signs
(K) Shortness of breath
(L) Before meals
(M) Foot
(N) Wheelchair
(O) As necessary
(P) Intake and output
(Q) Celsius degree
(R) Out of bed
(S) Follow up
(T) Ambulate, ambulatory

7. Explain how to give and receive an accurate oral report of a client's status

Multiple Choice

1. Which of the following is true of oral reports?
   (A) Home health aides should use facts when making oral reports.
   (B) Home health aides should use opinions when making oral reports.
   (C) Home health aides should make oral reports directly to clients' families.
   (D) Home health aides do not need to make oral reports; they only need to make written reports.

Name: _____

2. Which of the following should be reported to the supervisor immediately?
    (A) Trouble sleeping
    (B) Falls
    (C) Visits from family
    (D) Requests for help getting to the toilet

3. What is the best way for a home health aide to remember important details for an oral report?
    (A) Rely on his memory
    (B) Repeat the information to a friend
    (C) Write notes and use them for his report
    (D) Tell another home health aide to remind him

8. Explain objective and subjective information and describe how to observe and report accurately

Short Answer
Looking at the diagram, list examples of observations using each sense.

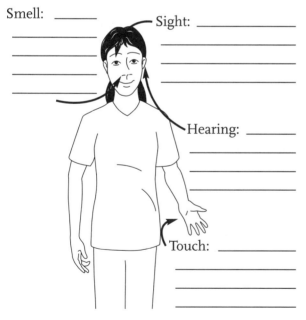

Smell: _____
_____
_____
_____
_____

Sight: _____
_____
_____
_____

Hearing: _____
_____
_____
_____

Touch: _____
_____
_____
_____

For each of the following, decide whether it is an objective observation (you can see, hear, smell, or touch it) or a subjective observation (the client must tell you about it). Write O for objective and S for subjective.

1. ____ Skin rash

2. ____ Crying

3. ____ Rapid pulse

4. ____ Headache

5. ____ Nausea

6. ____ Vomiting

7. ____ Swelling

8. ____ Cloudy urine

9. ____ Feeling sad

10. ____ Red area on skin

11. ____ Fever

12. ____ Dizziness

13. ____ Wheezing

14. ____ Chest pain

15. ____ Toothache

16. ____ Coughing

17. ____ Fruity breath

18. ____ Itchy arm

9. Explain why documentation is important and describe how to document visit records and incident reports

Multiple Choice

1. Which of the following statements is true of a client's medical chart?
    (A) A medical chart is the legal record of a client's care.
    (B) Not all care needs to be documented.
    (C) Documentation can be put off until the home health aide has time to do it.
    (D) Medical charts are not legal documents.

2. When should care be documented?
    (A) Before care is given
    (B) Immediately after care is given
    (C) At the end of the next day
    (D) Whenever there is time

3. An incident is
    (A) An accident or unexpected event that occurs during a visit
    (B) Any interaction between clients and home health aides
    (C) A normal part of personal care routines
    (D) Any event in a client's day

4. Which of the following would be considered an incident?
   (A) A client complains of a headache.
   (B) A client falls but is okay after the fall.
   (C) A client wants to watch TV in bed.
   (D) A client needs to be transferred from his bed to a chair.

Short Answer

Convert the following times to military time.

5. 2:10 p.m. _____

6. 4:30 a.m. _____

7. 10:00 a.m. _____

8. 8:25 p.m. _____

Convert the following times to regular time.

9. 0600 _____

10. 2320 _____

11. 1927 _____

12. 1800 _____

10. Demonstrate the ability to use verbal and written information to assist with the care plan

Short Answer

1. If an HHA is not sure what is important to mention in a care plan meeting, what should he or she do?

   _____

   _____

   _____

   _____

   _____

2. Why is accurate reporting by an HHA so important to the other members of the care team?

   _____

   _____

   _____

_____

_____

11. Demonstrate effective communication on the telephone

Short Answer
Read the home health aide's side of the following telephone conversations and think about how the HHA could have better presented herself on the phone.

Example #1 Leaving a message for the supervisor

Hi, who's this?

Could you get Ms. Crier on the phone, please? I need to talk to her.

She's not there? Do you know where she is? I really have to talk to her right now. My client forgot to take her pill this morning, and now she wants to take two. I don't know if that's okay or not, so that's why I need to talk to Ms. Crier.

Okay, well tell her Ella called and have her call me back. Ella. Ella Ferguson. I should be on the schedule.

The number? I don't remember what it is. Let me ask the client.

Okay, the number is 873-9042. I don't know how much longer I'll be here, but have her call me as soon as possible. Bye.

1. What did the home health aide do incorrectly in this phone conversation?

   _____

   _____

   _____

   _____

   _____

   _____

   _____

   _____

Example #2 Answering calls for the client

Hello? Mrs. Lee? No, she can't come to the phone right now. She's in the bathroom. Who's calling?

And your number?

Can I tell her what this is about?

Okay. I'll give her the message. Goodbye.

2. What did the home health aide do incorrectly in this phone conversation?

_____

_____

_____

_____

_____

_____

_____

_____

_____

_____

12. Describe cultural diversity and religious differences

Matching
Write the letter of the correct description beside each term related to the religious faith or belief. Use each letter only once.

1. ____ Agnosticism

2. ____ Atheism

3. ____ Buddhism

4. ____ Christianity

5. ____ Hinduism

6. ____ Islam

7. ____ Judaism

(A) Praying fives times a day facing Mecca and worshipping at mosques are part of this religion's practices

(B) Being baptized and receiving communion may be part of this religion's practices

(C) Believing that one does not know or cannot know if God exists

(D) Emphasizing meditation and believing that Nirvana is the highest spiritual plane a person can reach are part of this religion

(E) Believing in karma is a part of this religion

(F) Believing that God gave laws through Moses in the form of the Torah is part of this religion

(G) Actively denying the existence of any deity or higher power

13. List examples of cultural and religious differences

Short Answer

List three examples of dietary restrictions that may be due to religious beliefs.

1. _____

2. _____

3. _____

Multiple Choice

4. Which of the following is the name of a type of diet in which no animals or animal products are consumed, and animal products may not be used or worn?
(A) Fast
(B) Vegan
(C) Kosher
(D) Lacto-ovo vegetarian

5. Not eating food or eating very little food for a period of time is called
(A) Bingeing
(B) Restricting
(C) Fasting
(D) Testing

14. List ways of coping with combative behavior

Fill in the Blank

1. _____
behavior means being violent or hostile.

2. This behavior may be the result of

_____

affecting the brain, an expression of

_____, or

part of someone's

_____.

3. HHAs should try not to take combative behavior

_____.

4. HHAs should always

_____

combative behavior to their supervisors and

_____

it.

5. It is important for other members of the care team to be

_____ of

this behavior, even if the HHA does not find it upsetting.

_____
_____
_____
_____
_____
_____
_____
_____
_____
_____
_____

15. List ways of coping with inappropriate behavior

Short Answer

1. List three examples of client behavior that would be considered inappropriate.

_____
_____
_____
_____
_____
_____
_____
_____
_____
_____

2. For each example listed in #1, describe how an HHA should respond.

_____
_____

Name: _____

5

Infection Prevention and Standard Precautions

1. Define *infection prevention* and explain the chain of infection

Multiple Choice

1. The following are necessary links in the chain of infection. Which link is broken by wearing gloves, thus preventing the spread of disease?
   (A) Reservoir (place where the pathogen lives and grows)
   (B) Mode of transmission (a way for the disease to spread)
   (C) Susceptible host (person who is likely to get the disease)
   (D) Portal of exit (body opening that allows pathogens to leave)

2. The following are necessary links in the chain of infection. By getting a vaccination shot for hepatitis B, which link will a person affect to prevent him from getting this disease?
   (A) Reservoir (place where the pathogen lives and grows)
   (B) Mode of transmission (a way for the disease to spread)
   (C) Susceptible host (person who is likely to get the disease)
   (D) Portal of exit (body opening that allows pathogens to leave)

3. The most important thing a home health aide can do to prevent the spread of disease is to
   (A) Carry dirty linen close to her uniform
   (B) Put a cap on needles
   (C) Remove gloves before cleaning spills
   (D) Wash her hands

4. In what type of environment do microorganisms grow best?
   (A) In a warm, moist place
   (B) In a bright place
   (C) In a cool, dry place
   (D) In a frozen place

2. Explain Standard Precautions

Multiple Choice

1. Standard Precautions should be practiced
   (A) Only on people who look like they have a bloodborne disease
   (B) On every single person under a home health aide's care
   (C) Only on people who request that the home health aide follow them
   (D) Only on people who have tuberculosis

2. Standard Precautions include the following measures:
   (A) Washing hands after taking off gloves but not before putting on gloves
   (B) Wearing gloves if there is a possibility of coming into contact with blood, body fluids, mucous membranes, or broken skin
   (C) Touching body fluids with bare hands
   (D) Putting caps on used needles before putting them in the waste container

3. Which of the following is true of Transmission-Based Precautions?
(A) A home health aide does not need to practice Standard Precautions if he practices Transmission-Based Precautions.
(B) They are exactly the same as Standard Precautions.
(C) They are practiced in addition to Standard Precautions.
(D) They are never practiced at the same time that Standard Precautions are used.

4. How should sharps such as needles be disposed of?
(A) Sharps should be placed in blue recycling containers.
(B) Sharps should be placed in kitchen trash containers.
(C) Sharps should be placed inside used gloves and then put in the outside trash receptacle.
(D) Sharps should be placed in biohazard containers.

3. Define *hand hygiene* and identify when to wash hands

Multiple Choice

1. A home health aide (HHA) will come into contact with microorganisms
(A) Only in living areas of a house
(B) Only during direct contact with clients
(C) Only during personal care procedures
(D) Every time the HHA touches something

2. Centers for Disease Control and Prevention (CDC) defines hand hygiene as
(A) Handwashing with soap and water and using alcohol-based hand rubs
(B) Using only alcohol-based hand rubs
(C) Rinsing hands with cold water
(D) Not washing hands more than once per day

3. How long should a home health aide use friction when lathering and washing her hands?
(A) 2 minutes
(B) 5 seconds
(C) 18 seconds
(D) 20 seconds

4. Identify when to use personal protective equipment (PPE)

Short Answer
Make a check mark (✓) next to the tasks that require a home health aide to wear gloves.

1. ____ Contact with body fluids
2. ____ Hanging laundry
3. ____ When the HHA may touch blood
4. ____ Brushing a client's hair
5. ____ Assisting with perineal care
6. ____ Washing vegetables
7. ____ Giving a massage to a client who has acne on his back
8. ____ Assisting with mouth care
9. ____ Shaving a client

Multiple Choice

10. What type of personal protective equipment may be needed when caring for a client with a respiratory illness?
(A) Eyeglasses and mask
(B) Mask and foot covering
(C) Eyeglasses and gloves
(D) Mask and goggles

11. What type of personal protective equipment is used most often by caregivers?
(A) Gloves
(B) Mask
(C) Face shield
(D) Goggles

12. How many times can a gown be worn before it needs to be discarded?
(A) One time
(B) Two times
(C) Three times
(D) Four times

13. If blood or body fluids may be splashed or sprayed into the eye area, proper protection for the eyes is
(A) Gloves
(B) Mask
(C) Gown
(D) Goggles

Short Answer

14. What is the correct order for donning (putting on) PPE?

1st _____

2nd _____

3rd _____

4th _____

5th _____

15. What is the correct order for doffing (removing) PPE?

1st _____

2nd _____

3rd _____

4th _____

5th _____

5. Explain how to handle spills

Short Answer

Read the following scenario and answer the questions below.

Ritchie, a home health aide, takes a urine sample from his client, Mr. Velasquez. When he finishes, he accidentally knocks the container onto the linoleum floor. Some of the urine spills onto the floor. Ritchie quickly grabs a sponge and begins to wipe up the spill. When he is finished, he finds the mop, puts dishwashing soap into a bucket, and cleans the area again. When he is done mopping, he washes his hands.

Did Ritchie follow the proper spill-handling procedure? If not, what should Ritchie have done?

_____

_____

_____

_____

_____

_____

_____

_____

_____

_____

6. Explain Transmission-Based Precautions

Short Answer

List the type of precaution being described in each phrase below. Use an A for Airborne Precautions, a C for Contact Precautions, and a D for Droplet Precautions. Each letter may be used more than once.

1. ____ Transmission can occur when touching a contaminated area on the client's body

2. ____ Used when there is a risk of spreading an infection by direct contact with a person or an object

3. ____ Used to guard against tuberculosis

4. ____ Covering the nose and mouth with a tissue when a person sneezes or coughs, and washing hands immediately after sneezing are part of these precautions

5. ____ Helps prevent the spread of *Clostridium difficile* (*C. diff*) and conjunctivitis

6. ____ Used when the microorganisms are spread by droplets in the air that travel only short distances (normally not more than six feet)

7. ____ Microorganisms can be spread by coughing, sneezing, talking, or laughing

8. ____ Helps prevent the spread of illnesses transmitted through the air

9. ____ Helps protects against transmission of influenza

10. ____ May require the use of a special mask, such as an N95 or HEPA mask

7. Explain sterilization and disinfection

Short Answer

1. How does wet heat disinfect? How does dry heat disinfect?

    _____

    _____

    _____

    _____

    _____

    _____

2. What is the difference between sterilization and disinfection?

    _____

    _____

    _____

    _____

    _____

    _____

8. Explain how bloodborne diseases are transmitted

Multiple Choice

1. Bloodborne diseases can be transmitted by
    (A) Infected blood entering the bloodstream
    (B) Hugging a person with a bloodborne disease
    (C) Being in the same room as a person with a bloodborne disease
    (D) Talking to a person with a bloodborne disease

2. In health care, the most common way to be infected with a bloodborne disease is by
    (A) Contact with infected blood or certain body fluids
    (B) Hugging a client with a bloodborne disease
    (C) Being in the same room as a client with a bloodborne disease
    (D) Sexual contact with an infected client

9. Explain the basic facts regarding HIV and hepatitis infection

Multiple Choice

1. How does the human immunodeficiency virus (HIV) affect the body?
    (A) It cuts off blood supply to the brain.
    (B) It causes hearing impairment by damaging the inner ear.
    (C) It causes diabetes in otherwise healthy people.
    (D) It weakens the immune system so that the body cannot fight infection.

2. Which of the following is true of hepatitis B (HBV)?
    (A) HBV is caused by fecal-oral contamination.
    (B) There is no vaccine for HBV.
    (C) HBV is caused by jaundice.
    (D) HBV can be transmitted through blood or needles that are contaminated with the virus.

3. Employers must offer a free vaccine to protect home health aides from
    (A) AIDS
    (B) Hepatitis B
    (C) Hepatitis C
    (D) All bloodborne diseases

10. Identify high-risk behaviors that allow the spread of HIV

True or False

1. _____ A person is at risk for HIV or AIDS if he hugs an HIV-positive person.

2. _____ One way to protect against the spread of HIV or AIDS is to never share needles.

3. _____ Abstinence means having sex with only one person.

4. _____ A person is at risk for HIV if he has unprotected sex with an infected person.

5. _____ It usually takes six months for HIV to be able to be detected with a test.

6. ____ Having sexual contact with many partners puts a person at a high risk for HIV.

11. Demonstrate knowledge of the legal aspects of HIV, including testing

Short Answer

1. Why may the right to confidentiality be especially important to people who have HIV or AIDS?

_____
_____
_____
_____
_____
_____
_____
_____

2. What are two facts regarding HIV testing?

_____
_____
_____
_____
_____

12. Identify community resources and services available to clients with HIV or AIDS

Short Answer

1. What are three types of services that might be available for people who have HIV or AIDS?

_____
_____
_____
_____
_____

2. What is one way that a home health aide might be able to help a client look for community resources in his area?

_____
_____
_____
_____

13. Explain tuberculosis and list infection prevention guidelines

Multiple Choice

1. Tuberculosis may be transmitted
   (A) By coughing
   (B) By dancing
   (C) By wearing gloves
   (D) Through a protective mask

2. Tuberculosis is
   (A) A bloodborne disease
   (B) An airborne disease
   (C) A non-infectious disease
   (D) An untreatable disease

3. Someone with latent TB infection
   (A) Shows symptoms
   (B) Falls into a coma almost immediately
   (C) Cannot infect others
   (D) Can infect others

4. A person with TB disease
   (A) Can infect others
   (B) Does not show symptoms
   (C) Must eat only pureed foods
   (D) Cannot infect others

5. TB disease is more likely to develop in people
   (A) Who live near the mountains
   (B) Whose relatives had it when they were kids
   (C) Who have weakened immune systems
   (D) Who work alone

6. The word *resistant* in multidrug-resistant TB (MDR-TB) means that
   (A) Medications can no longer kill the specific bacteria
   (B) The infected person does not want to treat his or her disease
   (C) Doctors do not know what causes the disease
   (D) The infected person will die from the disease

14. Explain the importance of reporting a possible exposure to an airborne or bloodborne disease

Short Answer

How does a home health aide report possible exposure to an airborne or bloodborne disease?

_____

_____

_____

_____

_____

_____

_____

_____

_____

15. Discuss MRSA, VRE, and *C. difficile*

True or False

1. ____ Methicillin-resistant *Staphylococcus aureus* (MRSA) is almost always spread by direct physical contact.

2. ____ Once vancomycin-resistant *enterococcus* (VRE) is established, it is relatively easy to get rid of it.

3. ____ MRSA can be spread through indirect contact by touching objects contaminated by a person with MRSA.

4. ____ Handwashing will not help control the spread of MRSA.

5. ____ VRE causes life-threatening infections in people with weak immune systems.

6. ____ Frequent handwashing can help prevent the spread of VRE.

7. ____ Proper handwashing and handling of contaminated wastes can help prevent *Clostridium difficile* (*C. difficile*).

8. ____ Increasing the use of antibiotics helps lower the risk of developing *C. difficile* diarrhea.

9. ____ Both hand sanitizers and washing hands with soap and water are considered equally effective when dealing with *C. difficile*.

16. List employer and employee responsibilities for infection prevention

Short Answer
Read the following and mark ER for employer or EE for employee to show who is responsible for infection prevention.

1. ____ Immediately report any exposure to infection, blood, or body fluids.

2. ____ Provide personal protective equipment for use and train how to properly use it.

3. ____ Follow all agency policies and procedures.

4. ____ Take advantage of the hepatitis B vaccination.

5. ____ Provide continuing in-service education on infection prevention.

6. ____ Establish infection prevention procedures and an exposure control plan.

7. ____ Follow client care plans and assignments.

8. ____ Participate in continuing in-service education programs covering infection prevention.

9. ____ Use provided personal protective equipment as indicated or as appropriate.

10. ____ Provide free hepatitis B vaccinations.

Name: _____

6
Safety and Body Mechanics

1. Explain the principles of body mechanics

Labeling
Complete the illustration by labeling each part with the words listed below.

Alignment

Base of support

Center of gravity

Fulcrum

Lever

1. _____

_____

2. _____

3. _____

5. _____

_____

4. _____

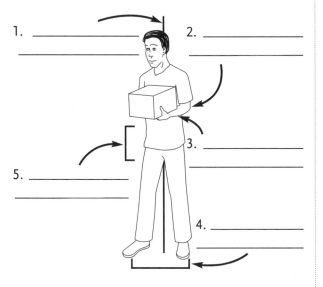

2. Apply principles of body mechanics to daily activities

Short Answer

1. Looking at the illustrations in the next column, which drawing shows the correct way to lift objects? Why is it correct?

_____

_____

_____
_____
_____
_____

A.   B.

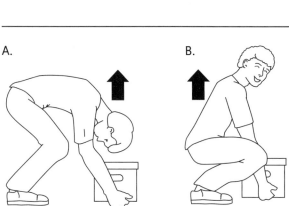

True or False

2. ____ Back injury is a serious problem that home health aides face.

3. ____ Using proper body mechanics can help save energy and prevent injury.

4. ____ When lifting an object, it is safer to hold it far away from the body.

5. ____ Feet should be pointed toward the object that a person is lifting.

6. ____ Keeping the feet close together gives the body the best base of support and keeps a person more stable.

7. ____ Lifting objects is safer than pushing objects.

8. ____ Knees should be bent when helping a client stand up.

9. ____ Twisting at the waist when lifting an object is safer than turning the entire body.

Name: _____

3. List ways to adapt the home to principles of proper body mechanics

Multiple Choice

1. If a home health aide (HHA) cannot reach an object on a high shelf, she should
   (A) Stand on tiptoes to reach it
   (B) Use a stepstool
   (C) Climb on a counter
   (D) Use an umbrella to reach it

2. When sitting for long periods of time, legs should not be crossed because
   (A) It disrupts the alignment of the body
   (B) It can wrinkle a person's clothing
   (C) It is unprofessional
   (D) HHAs must stand while working

3. To be more comfortable doing tasks that require standing for long periods of time, an HHA can
   (A) Sit down every five minutes
   (B) Hop on one foot
   (C) Jump up and down
   (D) Place one foot on a footrest

4. Frequently-used tools and supplies should be placed
   (A) On shelves or counters to reduce the need for bending
   (B) On the floor to reduce the need for straining to reach
   (C) In boxes where they will be out of the way
   (D) In the attic

5. To clean a bathtub, an HHA should
   (A) Bend over
   (B) Stand upright
   (C) Kneel
   (D) Sit inside the tub

4. Identify five common types of accidents in the home

Labeling
In the following illustrations, circle everything that you can find that is unsafe.

True or False

1. _____ Adjustable beds should be raised to their highest position each time the home health aide has finished with care.

2. _____ Older people are often more seriously injured by falls because their bones are more fragile.

3. _____ Older adults or people with loss of sensation due to paralysis or diabetes are at the greatest risk of burns.

4. ____ Clients should be sitting down before hot drinks are served to help prevent scalds.

5. ____ Infants should sleep on their backs to prevent sudden infant death syndrome (SIDS).

6. ____ To avoid choking, clients should eat in a slightly reclined position.

7. ____ To promote safety in the kitchen, pot handles should be turned out of sight and toward the back of the stove.

8. ____ A client who is ill and weak should not be left alone in a tub.

9. ____ Keeping the floor free from clutter and electrical cords helps prevent falls.

5. List home fire safety guidelines and describe what to do in case of fire

Short Answer

1. List four things that could be fire hazards.

_____

_____

_____

_____

_____

_____

_____

2. What is important to remember about clothing while working near the stove?

_____

_____

_____

_____

_____

3. How often should the smoke alarm be checked?

_____

4. RACE is an acronym that stands for

   R: _____

   A: _____

   C: _____

   E: _____

5. PASS is an acronym that stands for

   P: _____

   A: _____

   S: _____

   S: _____

6. Explain the fire safety technique "stop, drop, and roll."

_____

_____

_____

_____

_____

_____

_____

_____

6. Identify ways to reduce the risk of automobile accidents

Multiple Choice

1. When driving to a new client's house, a home health aide should
   (A) Study the map while driving there
   (B) Plan the route before leaving
   (C) Call the client to discuss the day's assignments beforehand
   (D) Text a friend for directions

2. While driving, it is best to
   (A) Keep eyes on the road and hands on the wheel
   (B) Call friends to pass the time more quickly
   (C) Drive quickly so that there will be more time at the client's home
   (D) Send text messages to confirm the day's schedule

3. When backing up in a car, the home health aide should
   (A) Only use the rearview mirror or camera
   (B) Back up quickly
   (C) Check the rearview mirror or camera and turn her head to look behind her
   (D) Use her instincts to tell her if someone is behind her

4. Driving at a safe speed means
   (A) Exceeding the speed limit
   (B) Making adjustments for road or weather conditions
   (C) Driving faster if it is snowing
   (D) Going ten miles per hour under the speed limit

5. Seat belts should always be worn because
   (A) They prevent accidents
   (B) They help protect a person if an accident occurs
   (C) They make the person look more professional
   (D) They make it safer to drive much faster

7. Identify guidelines for using a car on the job

True or False

1. _____ It is not necessary for a home health aide to keep track of the miles he drives for work.

2. _____ A home health aide's car should be serviced regularly.

3. _____ Proof of registration should be kept in the car at all times.

4. _____ Proof of insurance should be kept at home where it will be safe.

5. _____ Valuables should be put out of sight if they must be left in the car.

6. _____ All doors should be locked while driving and before leaving the car.

8. Identify guidelines for working in high-crime areas

Multiple Choice

1. A home health aide is going to visit a client who lives in a high-crime area. She has been to this client's apartment before, but today as she drives up, she notices three strange men standing on the sidewalk in front of the client's apartment. They are watching her as she slows down in front of the client's apartment. What should the home health aide do?
   (A) Ignore them and park the car
   (B) Keep driving past and use her phone to call her supervisor
   (C) Stop and ask them what they are doing in front of the client's apartment
   (D) Ask them to help her move items from her trunk into the client's house

2. A home health aide is getting ready to leave a client's home as it begins to get dark. Her client lives in a large house on a street that is not well-lit. She has parked next to the nearest street light, which is two houses down. What should she do on the way to her car?
   (A) Run to the car
   (B) Keep her keys inside her purse
   (C) Hold her purse or bag away from her body
   (D) Walk purposefully and confidently

7

Emergency Care and Disaster Preparation

1. Demonstrate how to recognize and respond to medical emergencies

Crossword

Across

4. Being mentally alert and having awareness of surroundings, sensations, and thoughts

6. What a home health aide must do after the emergency is over

Down

1. A type of wound that is considered a medical emergency

2. The person who responds to a medical emergency needs to assess the situation and assess this

3. In addition to checking for danger, noticing this is part of assessing the situation during a medical emergency

5. What needs to be reported when documenting an emergency

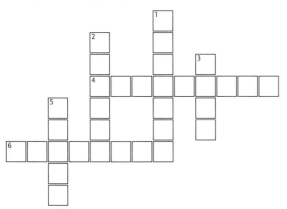

2. Demonstrate knowledge of first aid procedures

Multiple Choice

1. What should a home health aide do if a client needs CPR, but the HHA is not trained to perform CPR?
   (A) Perform CPR anyway
   (B) Perform CPR only with permission from the client's family
   (C) Perform CPR only if she thinks the victim will die if she does not
   (D) Do not perform CPR

2. If a home health aide has determined that an injured person is conscious, he should
   (A) Leave the victim because if he is conscious, that means he is all right
   (B) Tell the victim what is being done to help him
   (C) Call the victim's family to tell them what is happening
   (D) Call his friends to discuss how he felt when he saw that the person needed help

3. How can someone usually tell if a person is choking?
   (A) The choking victim will tell the person.
   (B) The choking victim will ask for food.
   (C) The choking victim will put his hands to his throat.
   (D) The choking victim will throw up.

4. How does a rescuer obtain consent to give a choking victim abdominal thrusts?
   (A) Rescuer asks victim's spouse to sign a consent form.
   (B) Rescuer calls family member to ask, "May I treat this person?"
   (C) Rescuer asks a lawyer.
   (D) Rescuer asks victim, "Are you choking?"

5. Signs of shock include
   (A) Pale or bluish skin
   (B) Lack of thirst
   (C) Happiness
   (D) Relaxation

6. If a home health aide suspects that a client is having a heart attack, she should
   (A) Give the client something cold to drink
   (B) Loosen the clothing around the client's neck
   (C) Encourage the client to walk around
   (D) Leave the client alone to rest

7. To control bleeding, a home health aide should
   (A) Use her bare hands to stop it
   (B) Lower the wound below the level of the heart
   (C) Hold a towel or clean cloth against the wound and press down hard
   (D) Give the client an aspirin for the pain

8. To treat a minor burn, the home health aide should
   (A) Use antibacterial ointment
   (B) Use grease, such as butter
   (C) Use ice water
   (D) Use cool, clean water

9. Which of the following is true of assisting a client who is having a seizure?
   (A) The home health aide should give the client water to drink.
   (B) The home health aide should hold the client down if he is shaking severely.
   (C) The home health aide should move furniture away to prevent injury to the client.
   (D) The home health aide should open the client's mouth to move the tongue to the side.

10. If a client faints, the home health aide should
    (A) Lower the client to the floor
    (B) Position the client on his side
    (C) Perform CPR immediately
    (D) Help the client stand up immediately

11. If a client has a nosebleed, what should be the first step that the home health aide takes?
    (A) Report and document the incident
    (B) Apply pressure consistently until the bleeding stops
    (C) Apply a cool cloth on the back of the neck, the forehead, or the upper lip
    (D) Elevate the head of the bed or tell the client to remain in a sitting position

12. If a client falls, the home health aide should
    (A) Wait until the end of the day to report the fall
    (B) Ask the client to get up to see if she can walk
    (C) Contact her supervisor to report the fall
    (D) Begin doing range of motion exercises while the client is on the floor

3. Identify emergency evacuation procedures

Short Answer

List five ways to plan for an emergency evacuation.

4. Demonstrate knowledge of disaster procedures

Multiple Choice

1. A disaster kit should be assembled before disaster strikes. Disaster supplies include
    (A) A change of clothing
    (B) A television set
    (C) Cosmetics and a hair dryer
    (D) Three pairs of shoes

2. In a disaster, a home health aide can stay informed by
    (A) Running out to buy a newspaper
    (B) Going outside to find his neighbors
    (C) Listening to a radio
    (D) Emailing friends

3. If a disaster is forecast, a home health aide can be prepared by
    (A) Doing her laundry
    (B) Cleaning her house
    (C) Knowing how to start a fire
    (D) Wearing appropriate clothing and shoes

4. In the event of a tornado, it is best to
    (A) Seek shelter inside, ideally in a steel-framed or concrete building
    (B) Stand flat against the wall next to the windows
    (C) Seek shelter in a mobile home
    (D) Seek shelter outside, ideally in trees or bushes

5. In case of lightning, it is best to
    (A) Find water and stay in the water
    (B) Stand by the largest tree in the area
    (C) Stand close to tall metal objects
    (D) Seek shelter in buildings

6. In case of floods, it is best to
    (A) Fill the bathtub with fresh water
    (B) Drink flood water to stay hydrated
    (C) Put electrical equipment in flood water to avoid fires
    (D) Turn off the gas by yourself

7. In case of earthquakes, it is best to
    (A) Stand on a tall piece of furniture to get as high as possible
    (B) Go outside to find the closest tall building
    (C) Stop under an overpass if in a car until the shaking stops
    (D) Get under a sturdy piece of furniture

Emergency Care and Disaster Preparation

8

Physical, Psychological, and Social Health

1. Identify basic human needs

Short Answer

1. List five basic physical needs that all humans have.

    _____

    _____

    _____

    _____

    _____

    _____

2. List six psychosocial needs that humans have.

    _____

    _____

    _____

    _____

    _____

    _____

3. Complete your own hierarchy of needs below. Some of the examples have already been completed for you.

Maslow's Hierarchy of Needs

Need

    (A) Need for self-actualization
    (B) Need for self-esteem
    (C) Need for love
    (D) Safety and security needs
    (E) Physical needs

Example of Need

    (A) I need the chance to learn new things.
    (B) I need to know that I am doing a good job.

    (C) _____

         _____

         _____

    (D) _____

         _____

         _____

    (E) _____

         _____

         _____

True or False

4. _____ Elderly people do not have sexual urges.

5. _____ Ability to engage in sexual activity continues unless disease or injury occurs.

6. _____ Clients have the legal right to choose how to express their sexuality.

7. _____ All elderly people have the same sexual behavior and desires.

8. _____ The home health aide should always knock and wait for a response before entering clients' bedrooms.

9. _____ If a home health aide encounters a sexual situation between consenting adults, he should ask them to stop.

10. _____ If a client is physically female but identifies as male, the home health aide should use both she and he when talking about the client.

Matching
Use each letter only once.

11. _____ Bisexual, Bi

12. _____ Cross-dresser

13. _____ Gay

14. _____ Gender identity

15. _____ Heterosexual (straight)

16. _____ Lesbian

17. _____ LGBT

18. _____ Sexual orientation

19. _____ Transgender

20. _____ Transition

(A) Acronym for lesbian, gay, bisexual, and transgender

(B) A person whose physical, emotional, and/or romantic attraction is for people of the opposite sex

(C) A person's physical, emotional, and/or romantic attraction to another person

(D) A person whose physical, emotional, and/or romantic attraction may be for people of the same gender or different gender

(E) A person whose gender identity conflicts with his or her birth sex (sex assigned at birth due to anatomy)

(F) A deeply felt sense of one's gender

(G) A person whose physical, emotional, and/or romantic attraction is for people of the same sex

(H) A heterosexual man who sometimes wears clothing and other items associated with women

(I) The process of changing genders, which can include legal procedures and medical measures

(J) A woman whose physical, emotional, and/or romantic attraction is for other women

2. Define holistic care

Short Answer

In your own words, briefly define holistic care.

_____

_____

_____

_____

_____

_____

3. Identify ways to help clients meet their spiritual needs

Place a check mark (✓) next to examples of appropriate ways to help clients with their spiritual needs.

1. _____ A client tells his home health aide (HHA) that he cannot drink milk with his hamburger due to his religious beliefs. He asks for some water instead. The HHA takes the milk away and brings him some water.

2. _____ A client tells her home health aide that she is a Baptist and wants to know when the next Baptist service will be. The HHA asks, "Why don't you just attend a Catholic service instead? I'm Catholic, and my church is close by."

3. _____ A client asks his HHA to read a passage from his Bible. The HHA opens the Bible and begins to read.

4. _____ A client wants to see a rabbi. His home health aide calls the rabbi he wants to see.

5. _____ A home health aide sees a Buddha statue in a client's bedroom. The HHA chuckles and tells the client, "This little guy is so cute."

6. _____ A spiritual leader is visiting with a client. The home health aide quietly leaves the room and shuts the door.

7. _____ A client tells his home health aide that he is Muslim. The HHA begins to explain Christianity to him and asks him to attend a Christian service just to see what it is like.

8. _____ A client tells her home health aide that she does not believe in God. The HHA does believe in God but does not argue with the client. The HHA listens quietly as the client explains her reasoning.

4. Discuss family roles and their significance in health care

Multiple Choice
Read each description below. Choose the term that best defines the type of family that is being described.

1. Mr. Dane's wife died giving birth to their twin girls. Mr. Dane never remarried and raised the girls himself.
   (A) Single-parent family
   (B) Nuclear family
   (C) Blended family
   (D) Extended family

2. Ms. Cone has lived with her best friend, Ms. Lawrence, since they graduated from college together. They both dated many men throughout their lives but were never married. Ms. Cone has a teenaged daughter who was raised in their household.
   (A) Single-parent family
   (B) Nuclear family
   (C) Blended family
   (D) Extended family

3. Mrs. Rose had three children with her first husband. She divorced him when their youngest child was two years old. Two years later she remarried, and she and her second husband raised her three children as well as one child from his first marriage.
   (A) Single-parent family
   (B) Nuclear family
   (C) Blended family
   (D) Extended family

4. Mrs. Parker was married to her husband for 30 years. They lived together with their two children.
   (A) Single-parent family
   (B) Nuclear family
   (C) Blended family
   (D) Extended family

5. Mr. Nicholson has been with his husband for 10 years. Their five-year-old son lives with them.
   (A) Single-parent family
   (B) Nuclear family
   (C) Blended family
   (D) Extended family

5. Describe personal adjustments of the individual and family to illness and disability

Short Answer

1. List three adjustments that family members may need to make due to a client's illness or disability.

   _____
   _____
   _____
   _____
   _____
   _____
   _____

6. Identify community resources for individual and family health

Short Answer

1. If a home health aide believes that a client needs help finding community resources, what should he do?

   _____
   _____
   _____
   _____

7. List ways to respond to emotional needs of clients and their families

Multiple Choice

1. A home health aide arrives at her client's house to find the wife, Mrs. McNabb, upset and close to tears. She tells the HHA that her husband simply will not eat his breakfast. When the HHA asks what she served him for breakfast, Mrs. McNabb begins to cry. What would be the best response by the HHA?
    (A) The HHA should ask her not to cry.
    (B) The HHA should ask her why she is crying over something so unimportant.
    (C) The HHA should reassure her that the HHA is there to help.
    (D) The HHA should tell her that her reaction is probably increasing her stress level.

2. The home health aide encourages Mrs. McNabb to talk about what is bothering her. Mrs. McNabb confesses that she is feeling very overwhelmed. What would be the best response by the HHA?
    (A) "I know just how you feel. My kids are a handful, too."
    (B) "It sounds like you are under a lot of stress. Can I help in some way?"
    (C) "Well, I work two jobs myself, and it's no big deal."
    (D) "I think attending church services more often would help."

3. Mrs. McNabb asks if the HHA can stay longer to help her out with the cooking and cleaning. What would be the best response by the HHA?
    (A) "I'll talk to my supervisor and see what she says. Maybe we can work something out."
    (B) "You can call a cleaning service for help."
    (C) "That's not in my job description."
    (D) "If you will pay me extra money, I can consider it."

9

Body Systems and Related Conditions

1. Describe the integumentary system and related conditions

Fill in the Blank

1. The largest organ and system in the body is the _____.

2. Skin prevents _____ to internal organs.

3. Skin also prevents the loss of too much _____, which is essential to life.

4. The skin is also a _____ organ that feels heat, cold, pain, touch, and pressure.

5. Blood vessels _____, or widen, when the outside temperature is too high.

6. Blood vessels _____, or narrow, when the outside temperature is too cold.

Labeling
For each position shown, list the areas at risk for skin breakdown.

Lateral Position

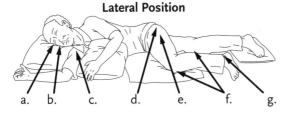

a.   b.   c.   d.   e.   f.   g.

7. Lateral Position

    a. _____

    b. _____

    c. _____

    d. _____

    e. _____

f. _____

g. _____

Prone Position

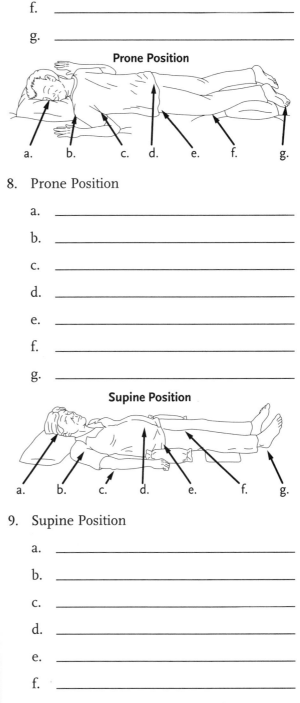

a.   b.   c.   d.   e.   f.   g.

8. Prone Position

    a. _____

    b. _____

    c. _____

    d. _____

    e. _____

    f. _____

    g. _____

Supine Position

a.   b.   c.   d.   e.   f.   g.

9. Supine Position

    a. _____

    b. _____

    c. _____

    d. _____

    e. _____

    f. _____

    g. _____

True or False

10. _____ With a stage 1 pressure injury, skin is intact but may be red or a different color than the surrounding area.

11. _____ Pressure injuries usually occur in areas of the body where bone lies close to the skin.

12. _____ Another name for pressure injuries is decubitus ulcers.

13. _____ Common sites for pressure injuries are the chest, nose, and hands.

14. _____ A contusion is a type of open wound.

15. _____ An open wound has skin that is not intact.

16. _____ Stasis dermatitis occurs due to a build-up of fluid in the lower legs and ankles.

2. Describe the musculoskeletal system and related conditions

True or False

1. _____ The body is shaped by muscles, bones, ligaments, tendons, and cartilage.

2. _____ The human body has 215 bones.

3. _____ Bones protect the body's organs.

4. _____ Two bones meet at a joint.

5. _____ Muscles provide movement of body parts.

6. _____ Range of motion exercises help prevent problems related to immobility.

7. _____ Atrophy occurs when the muscle weakens, decreases in size, and wastes away.

Multiple Choice

8. Arthritis is a general term referring to _____ of the joints.
   (A) Immobility
   (B) Inflammation
   (C) Redness
   (D) Stiffness

9. Pain and stiffness of osteoarthritis may increase with
   (A) Hot weather
   (B) Cold weather
   (C) An active lifestyle
   (D) Dehydration

10. Arthritis is generally treated with
    (A) Botox
    (B) Plastic surgery
    (C) Deep breathing exercises
    (D) Anti-inflammatory medications

11. What happens to the body when a person suffers from an autoimmune illness?
    (A) The circulatory system stops functioning and blood backs up into the heart.
    (B) The immune system attacks diseased tissue in the body.
    (C) The immune system attacks normal tissue in the body.
    (D) The integumentary system becomes diseased.

12. Rheumatoid arthritis affects the _____ joints first.
    (A) Smaller
    (B) Larger
    (C) Elbow
    (D) There is no typical progression.

True or False

13. _____ Muscular dystrophy (MD) is an inherited disease that causes gradual wasting away of the muscles.

14. _____ Most forms of MD become apparent in middle adulthood.

15. _____ Many forms of MD are very slow to progress.

16. _____ On average, a person who has amyotrophic lateral sclerosis (ALS) lives another 20 years after diagnosis.

17. _____ Having brittle bones due to osteoporosis means that bones become stronger and healthier.

3. Describe the nervous system and related conditions

Multiple Choice

1. The nervous system
   - (A) Gives the body shape and structure
   - (B) Controls and coordinates body function
   - (C) Is the largest organ in the body
   - (D) Pumps blood through the blood vessels to the cells

2. The basic unit of the nervous system is the
   - (A) Neuron
   - (B) Message
   - (C) Brain
   - (D) Spinal cord

3. The two main parts of the nervous system are
   - (A) Cardiovascular system and integumentary system
   - (B) Neurons and receptors
   - (C) The body and the brain
   - (D) Central nervous system and peripheral nervous system

4. The central nervous system (CNS) is made up of
   - (A) The brain and spinal cord
   - (B) Muscles and bones
   - (C) Neurons and receptors
   - (D) The heart and lungs

5. The peripheral nervous system (PNS) deals with the outer part of the body via the
   - (A) Brain
   - (B) Cerebrum
   - (C) Nerves
   - (D) Right hemisphere

True or False

Mark each of the following statements regarding CVA (stroke) with either a T for true or an F for false.

6. ____ Clients with paralysis or loss of movement will not need physical therapy.

7. ____ Range of motion exercises strengthen muscles and keep joints mobile.

8. ____ Leg exercises improve circulation.

9. ____ When helping with transfers or ambulation, the home health aide (HHA) should stand on the client's stronger side.

10. ____ The HHA should always use a gait belt for safety when helping a client who has had a stroke walk.

11. ____ The HHA should refer to the side that has been affected by stroke as the "bad" side so that clients will understand which side the HHA is talking about.

12. ____ Gestures and facial expressions are important in communicating with a client who has had a stroke.

13. ____ Clients who suffer confusion or memory loss due to a stroke may feel more secure if the HHA establishes a routine of care.

14. ____ Clients with a loss of sensation could easily burn themselves.

15. ____ Food should always be placed in the unaffected, or non-paralyzed, side of the mouth.

16. ____ When assisting with dressing a client who has had a stroke, the HHA should dress the stronger side first.

Short Answer

Read each of the following scenarios about caring for someone recovering from a CVA (stroke) and answer the questions.

17. Kate, a home health aide, is getting ready to prepare lunch for Mr. Elliot, who is recovering from a stroke. Mr. Elliot has difficulty communicating and also suffers from confusion. "Let's see," Kate says. "For lunch we can have soup, sandwiches, some leftover casserole, or I can make a salad. Now, what would you like to eat?" What is wrong with the way Kate is communicating with Mr. Elliot?

_____

_____

_____

_____

_____

_____

_____

_____

18. Mr. Elliot's wife comes home after running some errands and asks how her husband is doing. As she and Kate walk into the kitchen where Mr. Elliot is sitting, Kate says, "Mr. Elliot is having trouble today with his eating. Just look at him. He's spilled all over himself." What is wrong with what Kate has just said?

_____

_____

_____

_____

_____

_____

_____

19. Kate notices that Mr. Elliot seems to be having trouble saying words clearly. He is beginning to get frustrated because he cannot tell Kate what he wants. Kate decides to ask only yes or no questions, so she tells Mr. Elliot, "If you find it too difficult to speak right now, why don't you try nodding your head for 'yes' and shaking your head for 'no'?" What is Kate doing right?

_____

_____

_____

_____

_____

_____

True or False

Mark each of the following statements regarding Parkinson's disease with either a T for true or an F for false.

20. _____ Parkinson's disease is a progressive disease that causes a section of the brain to degenerate.

21. _____ Parkinson's disease causes a shuffling gait and a mask-like facial expression.

22. _____ Pill-rolling is something that people with Parkinson's disease must do before taking their medication.

23. _____ Clients with Parkinson's disease should be discouraged from performing their own care to save energy.

Fill in the Blank

Fill in the blanks for each of the following statements regarding multiple sclerosis (MS).

24. For a person who has MS, nerves cannot send _____ to and from the brain in a normal way.

25. Symptoms of MS include _____ vision, fatigue, tremors, poor balance, and difficulty walking.

26. The home health aide (HHA) should offer _____ periods as necessary for clients with MS.

27. The HHA should give clients plenty of time to _____ because people with MS often have trouble forming their thoughts.

28. _____ can worsen the effects of MS, so the HHA should remain calm and listen to clients when they want to talk.

True or False

Mark each of the following statements regarding head and spinal cord injuries with either a T for true or an F for false.

29. _____ The effects of a spinal cord injury depend on the location of the injury and the force of impact.

30. _____ The lower the injury on the spinal cord, the greater the loss of function will be.

31. _____ Quadriplegia is a loss of function of the lower body and legs.

32. _____ Rehabilitation is of little help for people who have had spinal cord injuries.

33. _____ Clients with head or spinal cord injuries will need emotional support as well as physical help.

34. _____ People with spinal cord injuries may not feel burns because of loss of sensation.

35. _____ The home health aide (HHA) should help clients change positions at least every two hours to prevent pressure injuries.

36. _____ Clients with spinal cord injuries should drink very little fluid to prevent urinary tract infections.

Short Answer
Answer the following question regarding amputation in the space provided.

37. What is phantom limb pain?

_____

_____

_____

_____

_____

Multiple Choice
Circle the letter of the answer that best completes the statement or answers the question regarding hearing impairment.

38. To best communicate with a client who has a hearing impairment, the home health aide (HHA) should
(A) Use short sentences and simple words
(B) Shout
(C) Approach the client from behind
(D) Raise the pitch of her voice

39. If a client is difficult to understand, the HHA should
(A) Pretend to understand the client so as not to hurt his feelings
(B) Mouth the words in an exaggerated way so that the client will mimic that behavior next time
(C) Ask the client to repeat what he said, and then tell the client what the HHA thinks she heard
(D) Ask the client to shout

Matching
For each of the following terms regarding vision impairment, write the letter of the correct definition from the list below. Use each letter only once.

40. _____ Cataract

41. _____ Farsightedness

42. _____ Glaucoma

43. _____ Nearsightedness

(A) Condition that causes increased pressure in the eye and may cause blindness

(B) The ability to see objects in the distance better than objects nearby

(C) Condition that causes cloudiness of the lens of the eye, which can cause loss of vision

(D) The ability to see objects that are nearby better than objects in the distance

4. Describe the circulatory system and related conditions

Multiple Choice

1. The two lower chambers of the heart are called
(A) Veins
(B) Cells
(C) Ventricles
(D) Pericardia

Name: _____

2. What functions as the pump of the circulatory system?
   (A) Heart
   (B) Lungs
   (C) Lymph
   (D) Blood

3. What occurs during the resting phase, or diastole?
   (A) Ventricles pump blood through the blood vessels.
   (B) The heart begins beating rapidly until the next contraction.
   (C) Circulation stops.
   (D) The chambers fill with blood.

4. Which of the following is one of the functions that the circulatory system performs?
   (A) Senses and interprets information from the environment
   (B) Supplies food, oxygen, and hormones to cells
   (C) Adds waste products to the cells
   (D) Processes carbohydrates and proteins to meet the body's energy needs

Matching
Use each letter only once.

5. ____ Angina pectoris

6. ____ Atherosclerosis

7. ____ Congestive heart failure

8. ____ Diuretic

9. ____ Hypertension

10. ____ Myocardial infarction

11. ____ Nitroglycerin

12. ____ Prehypertension

(A) Condition in which the heart fails to pump effectively, causing blood to back up into the lungs or the legs, feet, or abdomen

(B) The medical term for high blood pressure

(C) Chest pain, pressure, or discomfort

(D) Medication that relaxes the walls of the coronary arteries, allowing them to open and get more blood to the heart

(E) Condition in which blood flow to the heart muscle is blocked and the muscle cell dies

(F) Condition that indicates that although a person does not currently have high blood pressure, he is likely to have it in the future

(G) Medication that reduces fluid in the body

(H) Hardening and narrowing of the blood vessels

5. Describe the respiratory system and related conditions

Fill in the Blank

1. Respiration is the body taking in _____ and removing _____.

2. Respiration involves breathing in, or _____, and breathing out, or _____.

3. The _____ accomplish the process of respiration.

Multiple Choice

4. Clients with chronic obstructive pulmonary disease (COPD) have difficulty with
   (A) Breathing
   (B) Urination
   (C) Losing weight
   (D) Vision

5. For a person with COPD, a common fear is
   (A) Constipation
   (B) Incontinence
   (C) Not being able to breathe
   (D) Heart attack

6. The best position for a client with COPD is
   (A) Lying flat on his back
   (B) Sitting upright
   (C) Lying on his stomach
   (D) Lying on his side

7. Part of the home health aide's role in caring for a client with COPD includes
   (A) Being calm and supportive
   (B) Adjusting oxygen levels
   (C) Making changes in the client's diet
   (D) Doing everything for the client as much as possible

8. Emphysema usually develops as a result of chronic bronchitis and
   (A) Cigarette smoking
   (B) Alcohol use
   (C) Radiation therapy
   (D) Excessive weight loss

9. Chronic bronchitis and emphysema are grouped under
   (A) Chronic obstructive pulmonary disease, or COPD
   (B) Muscular dystrophy, or MD
   (C) Hypertension, or HTN
   (D) Coronary artery disease, or CAD

6. Describe the urinary system and related conditions

Short Answer

1. List two vital functions of the urinary system.

   _____

   _____

   _____

   _____

   _____

2. Why are women more likely to suffer from urinary tract infections than men?

   _____

   _____

   _____

   _____

   _____

3. In which direction should clients wipe after elimination to help avoid a urinary tract infection (UTI)?

   _____

   _____

   _____

Multiple Choice

4. Which of the following statements is true of urinary incontinence?
   (A) It is a normal part of getting older.
   (B) It is a risk factor for pressure injuries.
   (C) Drinking plenty of fluids makes the problem worse.
   (D) It is treated by using inhalers and doing deep breathing exercises.

5. Clients who are _____ are more likely to have urinary incontinence.
   (A) Bedbound
   (B) Active
   (C) Vegetarians
   (D) Strong

6. What can clients do to help prevent urinary tract infections?
   (A) Limit their fluid intake
   (B) Drink plenty of fluids rich in vitamin C
   (C) Increase their fiber intake
   (D) Avoid cleaning the perineal area

7. Describe the gastrointestinal system and related conditions

Crossword
Across

2. Pillows help keep the body in this position, which may be helpful when suffering from heartburn or gastroesophageal reflux disease

6. Disorder that occurs from decreased fluid intake, poor diet, inactivity, medications, aging, certain diseases, or ignoring the urge to eliminate

8. The process of expelling solid wastes made up of the waste products of food that are not absorbed into the cells

Name: _____

Down

1. Abbreviation for gastroesophageal reflux disease

3. Another name for the digestive system

4. The process of preparing food physically and chemically so that it can be absorbed into the cells

5. Artificial opening through the abdomen to which waste is diverted

7. Adding more of this into the diet may help treat hemorrhoids

Multiple Choice

9. When a client has gastroesophageal reflux disease, it is best for the client not to lie down until at least _____ hours after eating.
   (A) Two
   (B) Three
   (C) Four
   (D) Eight

10. Surgical treatment for ulcerative colitis may include a
    (A) Liver transplant
    (B) Colostomy
    (C) Heart bypass
    (D) Gastric sleeve

8. Describe the endocrine system and related conditions

Fill in the Blank

1. The endocrine system is made up of _____ in different areas of the body.

2. Chemical substances created by the body that control numerous body functions are called _____.

3. One function of the endocrine system is to regulate levels of phosphate and _____.

Multiple Choice

4. Diabetes is a condition in which the pancreas does not produce enough or properly use
   (A) Insulin
   (B) Glucose
   (C) Growth hormones
   (D) Adrenaline

5. Sugars collecting in the blood cause problems with
   (A) Breathing
   (B) Circulation
   (C) Pain level
   (D) Ambulation

6. Type 1 diabetes
   (A) Continues throughout a person's life
   (B) Is most common in the elderly
   (C) Is first treated with surgery
   (D) Does not require a change of diet

7. Changes in the circulatory system from diabetes can cause
   (A) Hair loss
   (B) Heart attack and stroke
   (C) Multiple sclerosis
   (D) COPD

8. The most common form of diabetes is
   (A) Insulin reaction
   (B) Gestational diabetes
   (C) Type 1 diabetes
   (D) Type 2 diabetes

9. Poor circulation and impaired wound healing may result in
(A) Urinary tract infections
(B) Cancer
(C) Leg and foot ulcers
(D) An autoimmune disease

10. Gangrene can lead to
(A) Loss of bowel control
(B) Peripheral vascular disease
(C) Congestive heart failure
(D) Amputation

11. What condition occurs when a person's blood glucose level is above normal but not high enough for a diagnosis of type 2 diabetes?
(A) Gestational diabetes
(B) Type 1 diabetes
(C) Pre-diabetes
(D) Hyperglycemia

12. Careful _____ care is especially important for people with diabetes.
(A) Foot
(B) Hair
(C) Facial
(D) Mouth

13. Diabetes can lead to the following complication:
(A) Insulin reaction
(B) Mastectomy
(C) Cancer
(D) Arthritis

14. What type of shoe material is best for people who have diabetes because the material helps prevent a build-up of moisture?
(A) Plastic
(B) Leather
(C) Glass
(D) Metal

15. For a client who has diabetes, where should lotion not be applied?
(A) Upper arms
(B) Lower back
(C) Back of the legs
(D) Between the toes

16. The meal plan for a client with diabetes may involve
(A) Counting carbohydrates
(B) Eating more sugary items
(C) Fasting for long periods to get blood glucose levels near normal
(D) Eating fatty foods to gain weight

17. Which of the following is true of a home health aide's responsibilities for a client who has diabetes?
(A) The HHA may need to inject insulin at regular times.
(B) The HHA may assist with the client's exercise program.
(C) The HHA will create the meal plan for the client.
(D) The HHA needs to cut the client's toenails when giving foot care.

18. What is another name for hypoglycemia?
(A) Sugar coma
(B) Diabetic ketoacidosis
(C) Insulin reaction
(D) Diabetes

19. What is a common symptom of hypothyroidism?
(A) Rapid heartbeat
(B) Weight gain
(C) High blood pressure
(D) Bulging eyes

9. Describe the reproductive system and related conditions

Multiple Choice

1. The reproductive system allows humans to
(A) Move and speak
(B) Create human life
(C) Think logically
(D) Fight disease

2. The male and female sex glands are called the
(A) Glands
(B) Ureter
(C) Gonads
(D) Urethra

3. Vaginitis may be caused by bacteria, protozoa, or
   (A) Hypertrophy
   (B) Lymph
   (C) Fungus
   (D) Discharge

4. Which of the following is a type of contact that can cause a sexually-transmitted infection (STI)?
   (A) Holding hands with an infected person
   (B) Having sexual intercourse with an infected person
   (C) Hugging an infected person
   (D) Dining with an infected person

True or False

5. ____ Gonorrhea is easier to detect in men than in women.

6. ____ Genital herpes can be cured with antibiotics.

7. ____ Syphilis is caused by bacteria.

8. ____ Symptoms of chlamydia include yellow or white discharge from the penis or vagina and a burning sensation during urination.

9. ____ Sexually-transmitted infections (STIs) can be transmitted by contact of the mouth with the genitals of an infected person.

10. ____ There is a vaccine available for human papillomavirus (HPV).

11. ____ Genital warts are a sign of genital HPV infection.

10. Describe the immune and lymphatic systems and related conditions

Short Answer

1. What is the difference between nonspecific immunity and specific immunity?

   _____

   _____

   _____

   _____

   _____

   _____

   _____

2. What two systems are related to the lymphatic system?

   _____

   _____

3. How is lymph fluid circulated?

   _____

   _____

   _____

   _____

True or False

4. ____ Human immunodeficiency virus (HIV) can only be transmitted through sexual contact.

5. ____ The first stage of HIV infection involves symptoms similar to flu.

6. ____ There is no known cure for acquired immune deficiency syndrome (AIDS).

7. ____ AIDS dementia complex occurs in the early stages of AIDS.

8. ____ There is a vaccine that can prevent a person from getting AIDS.

Multiple Choice

9. Care for the person who has HIV or AIDS should focus on
   (A) Helping to find a cure for HIV
   (B) Preventing visits from friends and family so as not to infect them
   (C) Providing relief of symptoms and preventing infection
   (D) Letting the person know that his life choices caused this disease

10. If a client with AIDS has a poor appetite, the home health aide (HHA) should
(A) Give the client an over-the-counter appetite stimulant
(B) Serve familiar and favorite foods
(C) Let the client know that if he does not eat, he might die
(D) Discuss this with the client's friends and family to see what they recommend doing

11. It is very important to follow safety guidelines when preparing food for the client who has AIDS because
(A) Foodborne illnesses can cause death
(B) The home health aide might become infected with HIV
(C) The home health aide might infect family members with HIV
(D) It is not important to follow safety guidelines regarding food preparation

12. Clients who have AIDS and have infections of the mouth and esophagus may need to eat food that is
(A) Spicy
(B) Low in acid
(C) Dry
(D) Very hot

13. Someone who has nausea and vomiting should
(A) Eat mostly dairy products
(B) Eat high-fat foods
(C) Drink liquids and eat salty foods
(D) Reduce liquid intake

14. Fluids are important for clients who have diarrhea because
(A) Diarrhea rapidly depletes the body of fluids
(B) Diarrhea can be prevented by drinking a lot of fluids
(C) Diarrhea is an infection that can be flushed out by fluids
(D) Diarrhea can make a client's throat dry

15. The following is helpful in dealing with neuropathy (numbness, tingling, and pain in the feet):
(A) Wrapping the feet in bandages
(B) Wearing tight shoes
(C) Using a bed cradle
(D) Tucking in bed sheets over the feet tightly

Short Answer
Mark an "X" beside the American Cancer Society's warning signs of cancer.

16. ____ Change in bowel or bladder function
17. ____ Difficulty breathing
18. ____ Dizziness
19. ____ Thickening or lump in breast
20. ____ Memory loss
21. ____ Change in appearance of wart or mole
22. ____ Joint aches
23. ____ Nagging cough
24. ____ Indigestion or difficulty swallowing
25. ____ Nausea
26. ____ Sweet, fruity breath odor
27. ____ Sores that do not heal
28. ____ Unusual bleeding or discharge
29. ____ Headache

Multiple Choice

30. The key treatment for malignant tumors of the skin, breast, bladder, colon, rectum, stomach, and muscle is
(A) Surgery
(B) Homeopathic pills
(C) Radiation
(D) Herbal remedies

31. Nausea, vomiting, diarrhea, hair loss, and decreased resistance to infection are all side effects of which treatment?
    (A) Surgery
    (B) Chemotherapy
    (C) Diet and exercise
    (D) Herbal remedies

32. This treatment method uses drugs to destroy cancer cells and limit the rate of cell growth:
    (A) Surgery
    (B) Chemotherapy
    (C) Radiation
    (D) Herbal remedies

33. This treatment method involves removing as much of the tumor as possible to prevent cancer from spreading:
    (A) Surgery
    (B) Chemotherapy
    (C) Radiation
    (D) Herbal remedies

34. This treatment method kills normal and abnormal cells in a limited area, sometimes causing skin to become sore, irritated, or burned:
    (A) Surgery
    (B) Chemotherapy
    (C) Radiation
    (D) Herbal remedies

35. To help promote proper nutrition for a client with cancer, the home health aide should do the following:
    (A) Use metal utensils when serving meals
    (B) Serve favorite foods that are high in nutrition
    (C) Restrict nutritional supplements
    (D) Serve foods with little nutritional content

36. If a client is experiencing pain, the home health aide should
    (A) Assist with comfort measures
    (B) Let the client know that there is little the HHA can do
    (C) Prescribe pain medication
    (D) Give the client a shot of pain medication

37. When providing skin care, which of the following should the home health aide do?
    (A) Use lotion regularly on dry skin
    (B) Remove markings that are used in radiation therapy
    (C) Clean the client's face with soap
    (D) Apply lotion to areas receiving radiation therapy

38. Which of the following should a home health aide do regarding oral care for a client with cancer?
    (A) Rinse the client's mouth with a type of commercial mouthwash
    (B) Use a soft-bristled toothbrush to brush the client's teeth
    (C) Use rubbing alcohol for any mouth sores the client has
    (D) Avoid giving the client oral care

39. Which of the following should the home health aide do when communicating with a client who has cancer?
    (A) Insist that the client tell the HHA what the client is going through
    (B) Let the client know about any new medications that might help the client
    (C) If the client is worried, tell him, "Don't worry. It will all be fine."
    (D) Listen to the client if he wishes to share his feelings

40. Mrs. Brady is a client who has cancer. She has a lot of visitors, and most of them call before they come over. One visitor has a habit of stopping by whenever she happens to be in the area, and today she has come at a very bad time for Mrs. Brady. What would be the best response by the HHA?
    (A) "Mrs. Brady enjoys your visits, but unfortunately this is not a good time for her. I'll certainly let her know you were here."
    (B) "You should think about calling before you come over because Mrs. Brady is often busy when you come by."
    (C) "Mrs. Brady does not like it when you drop in without calling first."
    (D) "Mrs. Brady does not enjoy surprise guests."

10

Confusion, Dementia, and Alzheimer's Disease

1. Discuss confusion and delirium

Short Answer

1. What are ten actions that a home health aide can take when helping care for a client who is confused?

_____
_____
_____
_____
_____
_____
_____
_____
_____
_____
_____
_____

2. Name four possible causes of delirium.

_____
_____
_____
_____
_____
_____
_____

2. Describe dementia

Multiple Choice

1. The ability to think logically and quickly is called
   (A) Cognition
   (B) Dementia
   (C) Awareness
   (D) Respiration

2. Cognitive impairment affects
   (A) Blood pressure
   (B) Motor skills
   (C) Concentration and memory
   (D) Diet and exercise

3. Home health aides can help elderly clients by
   (A) Doing as much as possible for them
   (B) Encouraging them to make lists of things to remember
   (C) Reminding them every time they forget something
   (D) Telling them to think as hard as they can

4. The most common cause of dementia is
   (A) Lewy body dementia
   (B) Alzheimer's disease
   (C) Reproductive cancers
   (D) Chronic obstructive pulmonary disease

3. Describe Alzheimer's disease and identify its stages

True or False

1. _____ A person with Alzheimer's disease is usually able to continue to use skills that he has used constantly over his lifetime.

2. ____ Each person with Alzheimer's disease will show the same symptoms at the same time during their lives.

3. ____ A home health aide should perform as many activities as possible for clients with Alzheimer's disease.

4. ____ Alzheimer's disease cannot be cured.

5. ____ Most people who have Alzheimer's disease will eventually be dependent on others for care.

4. Identify personal attitudes helpful in caring for clients with Alzheimer's disease

Short Answer
For each of the following, briefly describe why each attitude is helpful when caring for clients with Alzheimer's disease.

1. Do not take things personally.

_____

_____

_____

_____

_____

_____

_____

_____

2. Be empathetic.

_____

_____

_____

_____

_____

_____

_____

3. Work with the symptoms and behaviors noted.

_____

_____

_____

_____

_____

_____

4. Work as a team.

_____

_____

_____

_____

_____

_____

5. Be aware of difficulties associated with caregiving.

_____

_____

_____

_____

_____

6. Work with family members.

_____

_____

_____

_____

7. Remember the goals of the care plan.

_____

_____

_____

_____

_____

5. List strategies for better communication with clients with Alzheimer's disease

Short Answer

Read each scenario below and state an appropriate response.

1. Mrs. Hays, a client with AD, has awakened from her nap and does not recognize her room or anyone around her.

_____

_____

_____

_____

_____

2. Blake, a home health aide (HHA), has been trying to give Mr. Collins, a client with AD, a bath. Mr. Collins has become agitated and is asking Blake, "Who are you?" over and over again, although Blake has already identified himself twice.

_____

_____

_____

_____

_____

3. Mrs. Hays has been telling Blake a story about her niece. She is showing him a necklace that her niece gave her as a gift. She is having trouble remembering the word *necklace* and is getting upset.

_____

_____

_____

_____

_____

_____

4. Blake is helping Mr. Collins get ready to eat dinner with his family. Blake asks him to put his shoes on, but Mr. Collins does not understand what Blake wants him to do.

_____

_____

_____

_____

_____

_____

_____

Multiple Choice

5. When communicating with a client with AD, the home health aide (HHA) should
   (A) Quietly approach the client from behind.
   (B) Stand as close as possible to the client.
   (C) Communicate in a loud, busy place to help cheer up the client.
   (D) Speak slowly, using a lower voice than normal.

6. If a client is frightened or anxious, which of the following should the HHA do?
   (A) Check her body language so that she does not appear tense or hurried
   (B) Turn up the television or radio to try to distract the client
   (C) Use complex, longer sentences to calm the client
   (D) Give multiple instructions at one time so that the client has time to understand them

7. If a client perseverates, this means he is
   (A) Repeating words, phrases, questions, or actions
   (B) Suggesting words that sound correct
   (C) Hallucinating
   (D) Gesturing instead of speaking

8. If the client does not remember how to perform basic tasks, the HHA should
   (A) Do everything for him
   (B) Encourage the client to do what he can
   (C) Skip explaining each activity
   (D) Say "don't" as often as the HHA feels is necessary

6. Explain general principles that will help assist clients with personal care

Short Answer

1. What three principles will help home health aides give clients with dementia the best personal care?

   _____

   _____

   _____

   _____

   _____

   _____

7. List and describe interventions for problems with common activities of daily living (ADLs)

Short Answer

For each of the following statements, write good idea if the statement is a good idea for clients with Alzheimer's disease or bad idea if the statement is a bad idea.

1. Use nonslip mats, tub seats, and hand holds to ensure safety during bathing.

   _____

2. Always bathe the client at the same time every day, even if she is agitated.

   _____

3. Break tasks down into simple steps, explaining one step at a time.

   _____

4. Do not attempt to groom the client; people with Alzheimer's disease most likely do not care about their appearance.

   _____

5. Choose clothes that are simple to put on.

   _____

6. If the client is incontinent, do not give her fluids because it makes the problem worse.

   _____

7. Mark the bathroom with a sign as a reminder of when to use it and where it is.

   _____

8. Check the skin regularly for signs of irritation.

   _____

9. Follow Standard Precautions when caring for the client.

   _____

10. Do not encourage exercise as this will make the client more agitated.

    _____

11. Serve finger foods if the client tends to wander during meals.

    _____

12. Schedule meals at the same time every day.

    _____

13. Serve new kinds of foods as often as possible to stimulate the client.

    _____

14. Put only one kind of food on the plate at a time.

    _____

15. Use plain white dishes for serving food.

    _____

16. Do not encourage independence as this can lead to aggressive behavior.

    _____

17. Reward positive behavior with smiles and warm touches.

_____

8. List and describe interventions for common difficult behaviors related to Alzheimer's disease

Short Answer

For each description below, identify the behavior that the client with Alzheimer's disease is exhibiting, and describe one way of dealing with it.

1. Mrs. Donne gets upset at about nine o'clock every night. She repeatedly asks for snacks or drinks and refuses to go to bed.

    _____

    _____

    _____

    _____

    _____

2. Mr. Noble is playing chess with a friend who is visiting. Mr. Noble becomes angry when he loses the game. He shoves his friend and when the home health aide (HHA) approaches them, he tells her he is going to hit her.

    _____

    _____

    _____

    _____

    _____

3. Mrs. Martin gets very upset every time she sees the president on television. She yells at the screen and tells everyone what a poor state our country is in.

    _____

    _____

_____

_____

_____

_____

_____

4. Ms. Desmond used to enjoy talking to people and reading, but lately she does not seem to enjoy anything. She sleeps most of the day and never talks to anyone unless she is asked to.

    _____

    _____

    _____

    _____

    _____

    _____

5. Ms. Storey is walking around her home asking her home health aide what time it is. Even though she has been told several times, she still seems unsatisfied and keeps asking the question.

    _____

    _____

    _____

    _____

    _____

6. Mr. Montoya tells his home health aide that his wife has just called him on the phone. She is coming to pick him up and they are going to dinner at the restaurant where they went on their first date. The HHA knows that his wife has been dead for several years, and their favorite restaurant has long since closed down.

    _____

    _____

Name: _____

_____
_____
_____
_____

9. Describe creative therapies for clients with Alzheimer's disease

Short Answer
For each situation described below, identify the therapy that the home health aide is using.

1. Ms. Lee misses her husband, who has been dead for ten years, very much. Lisa, an HHA who works with her, always asks about her life with her husband and what it was like. Ms. Lee seems to enjoy telling Lisa stories about what they did when they were young and how happy she was when they were together.

_____
_____

2. Mr. Elking tells Lisa that he has a date with Rose, the pretty girl who lives across the street. He is going to take her dancing and out to a movie. Lisa knows that Rose lived in his neighborhood when he was a teenager and that he has not seen her for decades. Lisa knows that Mr. Elking rarely gets out of bed. Instead of correcting him, Lisa asks him what kind of movie they are going to see and what he thinks he should wear.

_____
_____

3. Mr. Tennant sometimes gets depressed, especially in the evenings. Lisa knows that he loves classical music, so she starts playing it for him in the evenings a little before he usually starts feeling sad. He sorts through albums and places them in stacks.

_____
_____

10. Discuss how Alzheimer's disease may affect the family

Short Answer

1. Why might families of people who have AD have a difficult time?

_____
_____
_____
_____
_____
_____
_____
_____

2. What two major resources affect the ability of clients' families to cope with AD?

_____
_____
_____

11

Human Development and Aging

1. Describe the stages of human development and identify common disorders for each group

True or False

1. ____ A child takes three years from birth to be able to move around, communicate basic needs, and feed himself.

2. ____ Infants develop from the hands to the head.

3. ____ Caregivers should encourage infants to stand as soon as they can hold their heads up.

4. ____ Putting an infant to sleep on its back can reduce the risk of sudden infant death syndrome (SIDS).

5. ____ Tantrums are common among toddlers.

6. ____ The best way to deal with tantrums is to give the toddler what he wants.

7. ____ Preschool children are too young to know right from wrong.

8. ____ Children learn language skills between the ages of 3 to 6.

9. ____ From the ages of 6 to 10 years, children learn to get along with each other.

10. ____ School-age children (ages 6 to 10) develop cognitively and socially.

11. ____ Preadolescents are often easy to get along with and are able to handle more responsibility than they were as younger children.

12. ____ Puberty is the stage of growth when secondary sex characteristics, such as body hair, appear.

13. ____ Most adolescents do not feel that peer acceptance is important.

14. ____ Adolescents may be moody due to changing hormones and body image concerns.

15. ____ Eating disorders are difficult to deal with but cannot be life-threatening.

16. ____ Due to changes they are experiencing, adolescents may become depressed and may attempt suicide.

17. ____ By 19 years of age, most young adults have stopped developing physically, psychologically, and socially.

18. ____ One developmental task that most young adults undertake is to choose an occupation or career.

19. ____ Middle-aged adults usually do not experience any physical changes due to aging.

20. ____ By the time a person reaches late adulthood, he must adjust to the effects of aging.

2. Distinguish between fact (what is true) and fallacy (what is not true) about the aging process

True or False

1. ____ Older adults have different capabilities depending upon their health.

2. ____ As people age, they often become lonely, forgetful, and slow.

3. ____ Diseases and illnesses are not a normal part of aging.

4. ____ Many older adults can lead active and healthy lives.

5. _____ Prejudice against older people is as unfounded and unfair as prejudice against racial, ethnic, or religious groups.

6. _____ Television and movies often present an accurate image of what it is like to grow old.

3. Discuss normal changes of aging and list care guidelines

Multiple Choice

1. Older adults experience changes in their skin due to aging because
   (A) Much of the fatty layer beneath the skin is lost
   (B) They develop allergies to skin care products
   (C) Circulation to the skin is increased
   (D) There is not enough moisture in the air

2. Normal changes of aging in the musculo-skeletal system include
   (A) Brittle bones
   (B) More flexible joints
   (C) Stronger muscles
   (D) Increased appetite

3. For clients who have poor vision, the home health aide should
   (A) Discourage wearing sunglasses outside
   (B) Keep eyeglasses clean
   (C) Dim the lights
   (D) Have them read a newspaper daily

4. For clients who are hard of hearing, the home health aide should
   (A) Speak in a low-pitched voice
   (B) Exaggerate her movements as she speaks
   (C) Shout to be heard
   (D) Remove excess earwax

5. For clients with a poor sense of taste and smell, the home health aide should
   (A) Stop seasoning foods
   (B) Make sure there are working smoke detectors in the home
   (C) Only feed them spicy foods
   (D) Perform oral care less often

6. For clients who have a poor sense of touch, the home health aide should
   (A) Serve food at hotter temperatures
   (B) Bathe these clients less often
   (C) Keep heating pads on the skin longer
   (D) Be careful when serving hot drinks

7. Clients with heart conditions should
   (A) Exercise vigorously to regain strength
   (B) Avoid vigorous activity
   (C) Avoid doing any activity
   (D) Stand up quickly to avoid dizziness

8. If a client is cold due to poor circulation, the best response by the home health aide is to
   (A) Use a heating pad on the client's legs and arms
   (B) Remove the client's slippers
   (C) Layer the client's clothing
   (D) Put a hot water bottle on the client's feet

9. The best position for clients who have diffi-culty breathing is usually
   (A) Lying on the left side
   (B) Lying on the stomach
   (C) Lying flat on the back
   (D) Sitting upright

10. Older clients may need to urinate more fre-quently due to
    (A) The bladder not being able to hold as much urine
    (B) Drinking more fluids than younger adults
    (C) Incontinence
    (D) Being thirsty more often

11. Which of the following statements is true of urinary incontinence?
    (A) It is a normal part of aging.
    (B) It could be a sign of illness.
    (C) It occurs when a person drinks too much fluid.
    (D) It is always accompanied by constipation.

12. Constipation could be the result of
    (A) Faster digestion process due to aging
    (B) Eating too much food during the day
    (C) Getting too much water or fiber in the diet
    (D) Slower peristalsis

13. Because insulin production lessens due to aging, some clients may
    (A) Need to take insulin to regulate blood sugar
    (B) Need to fast each day
    (C) Eat more sugary foods to increase insulin levels
    (D) Have the home health aide give hormone injections

14. Normal changes in the reproductive system due to aging often result in
    (A) Loss of sexual drive
    (B) Thinning of vaginal walls in females
    (C) Inappropriate sexual advances
    (D) Decrease in the size of the prostate gland in males

15. Which of the following is a result of a weakened immune system due to normal changes of aging?
    (A) Increased risk of infection
    (B) More bouts of insomnia
    (C) Lower risk of falls
    (D) Increased risk of hypertension

16. Insomnia, withdrawal, and moodiness are common signs of
    (A) Anorexia
    (B) Depression
    (C) Confusion
    (D) Forgetfulness

17. Which of the following is a healthy way for a home health aide (HHA) to respond to clients' lifestyle changes due to aging?
    (A) Assume that most elderly clients are depressed and need medication
    (B) Insist that clients discuss their feelings
    (C) Listen to clients who want to discuss their feelings
    (D) Talk about the HHA's own problems to make them forget theirs

18. What is the most important thing to do if a home health aide observes any changes in her client's condition?
    (A) Report it to her supervisor
    (B) Report it to her supervisor
    (C) Report it to her supervisor
    (D) All of the above

4. Identify attitudes and habits that promote health

Short Answer

List six things that home health aides can do to encourage clients to stay active, maintain self-esteem, and live independently.

_____

_____

_____

_____

_____

_____

_____

_____

Human Development and Aging

Name: _____

12

Positioning, Transfers, and Ambulation

1. Explain positioning and describe how to safely position clients

Labeling
Label each position that is illustrated below and describe appropriate comfort measures for each.

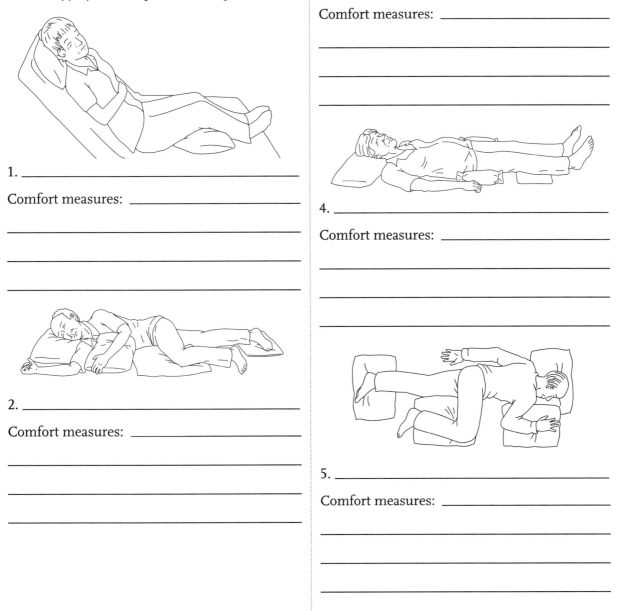

1. _____

Comfort measures: _____

_____

_____

_____

2. _____

Comfort measures: _____

_____

_____

_____

3. _____

Comfort measures: _____

_____

_____

_____

4. _____

Comfort measures: _____

_____

_____

_____

5. _____

Comfort measures: _____

_____

_____

_____

Positioning, Transfers, and Ambulation

Multiple Choice

6. Why do clients who spend a lot of time in bed or wheelchairs need to be repositioned often?
    (A) Repositioning helps prevent boredom.
    (B) They are at risk for skin breakdown and pressure injuries.
    (C) Repositioning makes it easier to talk to visitors.
    (D) Their family members will usually sue the agency if they are not.

7. In this position, the client is lying on either side:
    (A) Supine
    (B) Lateral
    (C) Prone
    (D) Fowler's

8. In this position, the client is lying on his stomach:
    (A) Sims'
    (B) Lateral
    (C) Prone
    (D) Fowler's

9. Logrolling is
    (A) A way to measure a bedbound client's weight
    (B) One way to record vital signs for clients who cannot get out of bed easily
    (C) Moving a client as a unit without disturbing alignment
    (D) A special method of bedmaking

10. Dangling is
    (A) Lying in the supine position
    (B) Doing a few sit-ups in bed to get used to the upright position
    (C) Elevating the client's feet with pillows
    (D) A way to help clients regain balance before standing up

11. A client in the Fowler's position is
    (A) In a semi-sitting position (45 to 60 degrees)
    (B) Lying flat on his back
    (C) In a left side-lying position
    (D) Lying on his stomach

12. A draw sheet is used to
    (A) Make changing the bottom bed sheet easier
    (B) Help clients sleep better
    (C) Reposition clients without causing shearing
    (D) Prevent incontinence

2. Describe how to safely transfer clients

Multiple Choice

1. Which of the following is an accurate guideline regarding how a home health aide should work with clients in wheelchairs?
    (A) Before transferring a client, the HHA should make sure the wheelchair is unlocked and movable.
    (B) The HHA should check the client's alignment in the chair after a transfer is complete.
    (C) To fold a standard wheelchair, the HHA should turn it upside-down to make the seat flatten.
    (D) All clients will need their HHA to transfer them to their wheelchairs.

2. Some clients have a side of the body that is weaker than the other one. The weaker side of the body should be referred to as the
    (A) Released side
    (B) Separated side
    (C) Ambulated side
    (D) Involved side

3. When applying a transfer belt, the home health aide should place it
    (A) Around the wheelchair's backrest
    (B) Underneath the client's clothing, on bare skin
    (C) Over the client's clothing and around the waist
    (D) Around the home health aide's waist so the client can hold on to it

4. The following piece of equipment may be used to help transfer a client who is unable to bear weight on her legs:
   (A) Sling
   (B) Slide board
   (C) Wheeled table
   (D) Folded blanket

5. Which of the following statements is true of using mechanical, or hydraulic, lifts to assist with transfers?
   (A) When doing this type of transfer, it is safer for one person to transfer the client by himself.
   (B) The legs of the stand need to be closed, in their narrowest position, before helping the client into the lift.
   (C) Lifts help prevent injury to the home health aide and the client.
   (D) It is best to use mechanical lifts when moving the client a long distance.

6. When transferring clients who have a one-sided weakness, which side moves first?
   (A) Left side
   (B) Either side
   (C) Weaker side
   (D) Stronger side

3. Discuss how to safely ambulate a client

Multiple Choice

1. If a client starts to fall while walking, the best response by the home health aide would be to
   (A) Widen his stance and bring the client's body close to him
   (B) Catch the client under the arms to stop the fall
   (C) Move out of the way to allow the client to fall since he could be injured trying to break the fall
   (D) Let the client fall on top of him to break the fall

2. If a client falls, what is the first thing the home health aide should do?
   (A) Help the client get up and into bed
   (B) Help the client walk around the room until she is steady
   (C) Call for help if a family member is around
   (D) Give the client ibuprofen and perform a physical examination to check for broken bones

3. A client who has some difficulty with balance but can bear weight on both legs should use a
   (A) Walker
   (B) Crutch
   (C) Wheelchair
   (D) Transfer board

4. Ambulation is another word for
   (A) Walking
   (B) Moving in a wheelchair
   (C) Riding in an ambulance
   (D) Logrolling

5. In addition to a gait belt, what equipment should the home health aide have when assisting a client to ambulate?
   (A) Mechanical lift
   (B) Rocking chair
   (C) Extra pillows
   (D) Nonskid shoes

6. If the client is unable to stand without help, the home health aide should
   (A) Hold the client close to the home health aide's center of gravity
   (B) Tell the client to stand on the count of three
   (C) Brace the client's lower extremities
   (D) Adjust the bed to its highest position

7. When helping a client who is visually impaired to walk, it is important for the home health aide to
   (A) Keep the client in front of her
   (B) Let the client walk beside and slightly behind her
   (C) Walk quickly
   (D) Avoid mentioning stepping up or down

8. Which of the following assistive devices for walking has four rubber-tipped feet?
(A) C cane
(B) Quad cane
(C) Crutch
(D) Gait belt

9. When using a cane, the client should place it on his _____ side.
(A) Left
(B) Right
(C) Weaker
(D) Stronger

4. List ways to make clients more comfortable

Short Answer

1. List four things the home health aide can do to provide for the comfort and safety of clients in and around the bed.

_____

_____

_____

_____

_____

_____

_____

_____

_____

_____

_____

2. Name two benefits of giving a client a back rub.

_____

_____

_____

_____

_____

_____

_____

_____

_____

_____

Matching
Use each letter only once.

3. ____ Abduction pillows

4. ____ Backrests

5. ____ Bed cradles

6. ____ Bed tables

7. ____ Draw sheets

8. ____ Footboards

9. ____ Handrolls

10. ____ Orthotic devices

11. ____ Trochanter rolls

(A) Placed against the feet to keep them properly aligned and to prevent foot drop

(B) Keep bed covers from resting on the legs and feet

(C) Used to help clients who cannot help with turning or moving up in bed; helps prevent skin damage from shearing

(D) Keep the hand and/or fingers in a normal, natural position

(E) Keep hips and legs from turning outward

(F) Help support and align a limb and improve its functioning (e.g., a splint)

(G) Made of pillows, cardboard, or wood, they provide support for the back

(H) Keep food or other often-used items close to the client while he is in bed; one option can be made at home using a cardboard box

(I) Special pillows used to keep the hips in proper position after hip surgery

13

Personal Care Skills

1. Describe the home health aide's role in assisting clients with personal care

Short Answer

1. Why should the home health aide explain to the client what he will be doing before beginning a task?

_____

_____

_____

_____

2. List three things that the home health aide should observe when providing or assisting with personal care.

_____

_____

_____

_____

2. Explain guidelines for assisting with bathing

True or False

1. _____ Bathing promotes health and removes perspiration and dirt from the skin.

2. _____ The axillae (underarms) should be washed three times per week.

3. _____ When washing a client's eyes and face, the home health aide should use a warm, soapy washcloth.

4. _____ The perineum should be washed every day.

5. _____ Older skin produces more perspiration than younger skin.

6. _____ The client should test the temperature of the water before bathing because she is best able to choose a comfortable water temperature.

7. _____ When washing a female's perineal area, the home health aide should wipe from back to front.

8. _____ Using bath oils during baths is helpful for clients with dry skin.

9. _____ Checking to make sure the room is warm enough for the client before bathing is important.

10. _____ Before performing perineal care, the home health aide should change his gloves.

3. Describe guidelines for assisting with grooming

True or False

1. _____ It is better for a client to wear nightclothes during the day, rather than regular clothes, because nightclothes are more comfortable.

2. _____ The home health aide, rather than the client, should choose a client's clothing for the day because the home health aide can do it faster.

3. _____ Front-fastening bras are easier for clients to work by themselves.

4. _____ When dressing a client who has a weakness or paralysis on one side, the home health aide should dress the stronger side first.

5. _____ Clothing that is a size smaller than the client normally wears is easier to put on.

6. ____ If a client has a weaker left arm due to a stroke, the home health aide should refer to it as the "bad" arm, because that term is easily understood.

7. ____ As long as the client has no cuts on his face, the home health aide does not need to wear gloves while shaving him.

8. ____ Lice eggs are brown or white.

9. ____ When providing foot care, the home health aide should put lotion on dry areas between the toes.

10. ____ When assisting with grooming, the home health aide should let the client do all that he can for himself.

4. Identify guidelines for oral care

Multiple Choice

1. When must oral care be done?
   (A) After the last snack of the day
   (B) Before lunch is eaten
   (C) After the afternoon snack
   (D) Before dinner is served

2. The inhalation of food, fluid, or foreign material into the lungs is called
   (A) Peristalsis
   (B) Aspiration
   (C) Pediculosis
   (D) Hygiene

3. In which position should an unconscious client be placed before giving oral care?
   (A) Sitting upright
   (B) Flat on his back
   (C) Reclining slightly in a chair
   (D) Turned on his side

4. Dentures must be handled carefully because
   (A) A client cannot eat without them
   (B) They do not cost much
   (C) A client will look unattractive without them
   (D) They are sharp

5. How should dentures be stored?
   (A) In a denture cup
   (B) In ice water
   (C) Wrapped in a paper towel
   (D) In hot water

6. If a home health aide is removing a client's dentures, the client should be
   (A) Lying down on his back
   (B) Standing
   (C) Sitting upright
   (D) Lying down on his side

5. Explain care guidelines for prosthetic devices

True or False

1. ____ Hearing aids should be soaked in water before cleaning them.

2. ____ When cleaning the eyelid after an artificial eye is removed, the home health aide should wipe gently from the outer area toward the inner area.

3. ____ Prostheses are relatively inexpensive and are easy to replace.

4. ____ Artificial eyes are held in place by a special type of glue.

5. ____ In general, hearing aids should be cleaned daily.

6. ____ A prosthesis is a device that replaces a body part that is missing or deformed because of an accident, injury, illness, or birth defect.

7. ____ Artificial eyes should be rinsed in rubbing alcohol to prevent infection.

8. ____ If a prosthesis is broken, it is best for the home health aide to try to repair it before bothering her supervisor about it.

9. ____ When observing the skin on the stump, it is important that the home health aide check for signs of skin breakdown caused by pressure and abrasion.

6. Explain guidelines for assisting with toileting

Multiple Choice

1. A fracture pan is used for urination with
   (A) Any client who cannot get out of bed
   (B) Clients who cannot raise their hips
   (C) Clients who have problems with incontinence
   (D) Clients who have difficulty urinating

2. Men will generally use a _____ for urination when they cannot get out of bed.
   (A) Urinal
   (B) Fracture pan
   (C) Toilet
   (D) Portable commode

3. Clients who can get out of bed but cannot walk to the bathroom may use a(n)
   (A) Toilet
   (B) Urinal
   (C) Portable commode
   (D) Indwelling catheter

4. The best position for bowel elimination is
   (A) Squatting and leaning forward
   (B) Lying flat on the back
   (C) Lying on the left side
   (D) Leaning backward

5. Which of the following statements is true of properly positioning a standard bedpan?
   (A) A standard bedpan should be positioned with the narrower end aligned with the client's buttocks.
   (B) A standard bedpan can be positioned either toward the foot or head of the bed.
   (C) A standard bedpan should be positioned with the wider end aligned with the client's buttocks.
   (D) A standard bedpan should be positioned sideways and slightly tilted.

7. Describe how to dispose of body wastes

Short Answer

1. How must washcloths that have been used to clean perineal areas be washed?

   _____

   _____

2. Why must gloves be worn when handling bedpans, urinals, or basins that contain wastes?

   _____

   _____

   _____

   _____

Name: _____

Personal Care Skills

14

Core Healthcare Skills

1. Explain the importance of monitoring vital signs

Short Answer

1. What might changes in vital signs indicate?

_____

_____

_____

_____

2. Which changes should be immediately reported to a supervisor?

_____

_____

_____

_____

_____

_____

3. What are five sites for measuring body temperature?

_____

_____

_____

_____

_____

_____

Short Answer

Mark an X by each person for whom an oral temperature should NOT be taken.

4. _____ Person is disoriented.

5. _____ Person has sores in his mouth.

6. _____ Person is 40 years old.

7. _____ Person is unconscious.

8. _____ Person has a broken leg.

9. _____ Person is likely to have a seizure.

10. _____ Person has a nasogastric tube.

11. _____ Person has had children.

Short Answer

For each of the illustrations of mercury-free thermometers shown below, write the temperature reading to the nearest tenth degree in the blanks provided.

12. _____

13. _____

14. _____

15. _____

16. _____

17. _____

Name: _____

18. _____

19. _____

20. _____

21. _____

Multiple Choice

22. Which of the following is the normal temperature range for the oral method?
    (A) 90.6–94.6 degrees Fahrenheit
    (B) 93.6–97.9 degrees Fahrenheit
    (C) 98.6–100.6 degrees Fahrenheit
    (D) 97.6–99.6 degrees Fahrenheit

23. Which of the following thermometers is used to take a temperature in the ear?
    (A) Oral thermometer
    (B) Rectal thermometer
    (C) Axillary thermometer
    (D) Tympanic thermometer

24. Which of the following temperature sites is another word for the armpit area?
    (A) Oral
    (B) Rectal
    (C) Axilla
    (D) Tympanic

25. Which temperature site is considered to be the most accurate?
    (A) Oral
    (B) Rectal
    (C) Axillary
    (D) Tympanic

26. What is the main reason mercury-free thermometers considered better to use than mercury thermometers?
    (A) They do not contain mercury, which is a dangerous and toxic substance.
    (B) They are much smaller than mercury thermometers.
    (C) They are read differently than mercury thermometers.
    (D) They are less expensive than mercury thermometers.

27. What is the most common site for monitoring the pulse?
    (A) Apical pulse
    (B) Femoral pulse
    (C) Pedal pulse
    (D) Radial pulse

28. For adults, the normal pulse rate is
    (A) 20–40 beats per minute
    (B) 40–60 beats per minute
    (C) 60–100 beats per minute
    (D) 90–120 beats per minute

29. The medical term for difficulty breathing is
    (A) Dyspeptic
    (B) Dyspnea
    (C) Dysphagia
    (D) Dystolic

30. The medical term for rapid respirations is
    (A) Apnea
    (B) Eupnea
    (C) Orthopnea
    (D) Tachypnea

31. The normal respiration rate for adults ranges from
    (A) 5 to 10 breaths per minute
    (B) 7 to 11 breaths per minute
    (C) 12 to 20 breaths per minute
    (D) 25 to 32 breaths per minute

32. Why is it important for the home health aide (HHA) to observe respirations without letting the client know what she is doing?
   (A) People may breathe more quickly if they know they are being observed.
   (B) People will hold their breath if they know what the HHA wants to measure.
   (C) The procedure goes much faster if the client is unaware of what is happening.
   (D) Observing respirations is a painful process for most people.

33. Which of the following is considered a high blood pressure reading?
   (A) 120/79
   (B) 140/90
   (C) 110/70
   (D) 100/89

34. Which of the following is used to measure blood pressure?
   (A) Sphygmomanometer
   (B) Urostoscope
   (C) Reflex hammer
   (D) Otoscope

35. The second measurement of blood pressure reflects the phase when the heart relaxes. It is called the _____ phase.
   (A) Systolic
   (B) Mercurial
   (C) Hyperbolic
   (D) Diastolic

36. Blood pressure measurements are recorded as
   (A) Rhythms
   (B) Fractions
   (C) Decimals
   (D) Equations

37. Which measurement of blood pressure is always higher than the other?
   (A) Systolic
   (B) Dystemic
   (C) Diastolic
   (D) Systemic

Short Answer

For each of the gauges shown below, record the blood pressure shown and answer the question.

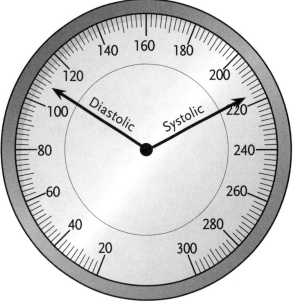

38. _____
   Is this reading within normal range?
   _____

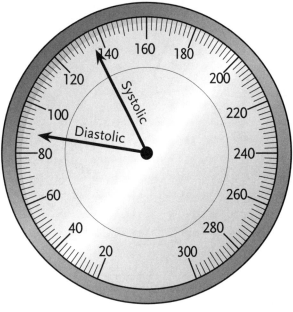

39. _____
   Is this reading within normal range?

Name: _____

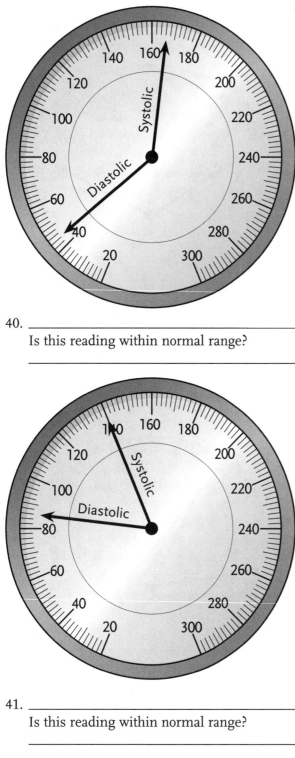

40. _____
Is this reading within normal range?
_____

41. _____
Is this reading within normal range?
_____

Short Answer

42. If a client complains of pain, what questions should the home health aide ask to get the most accurate information?
_____
_____

_____ (lines)

Short Answer
Looking at each of the readings shown below, record the weight shown.

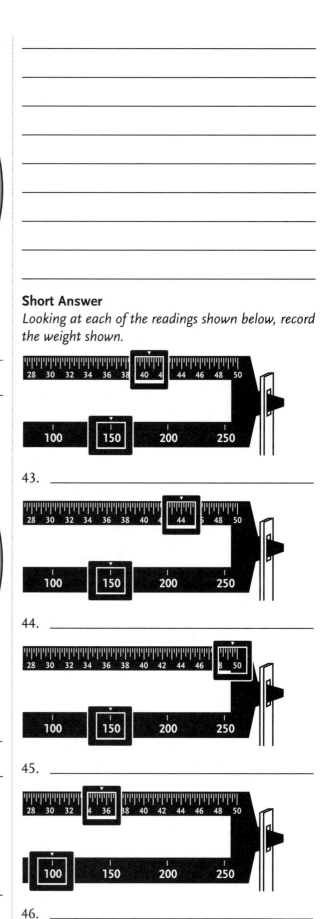

43. _____

44. _____

45. _____

46. _____

2. List three types of specimens that may be collected from a client

Matching
Use each letter only once.

1. ____ Clean-catch specimen

2. ____ Hat

3. ____ Routine urine specimen

4. ____ Specimen

5. ____ Sputum specimen

6. ____ Stool specimen

(A) Collection container put into toilet to collect specimens

(B) Urine and toilet paper should not be included with this specimen

(C) A sample that is used for analysis in order to try to make a diagnosis

(D) Urine sample collected any time the client voids

(E) Excludes first and last urine voided from the sample

(F) A specimen of thick mucus that is best collected in the early morning

3. Describe the importance of fluid balance and explain intake and output (I&O)

True or False

1. ____ Fluids come in the form of liquids a person drinks, as well as semi-liquid foods such as soup or gelatin.

2. ____ The fluid a person consumes is called intake or input.

3. ____ All of the body's fluid output is in the form of urine.

4. ____ Fluid balance is taking in and eliminating the same amounts of fluid.

5. ____ Most people need to consciously monitor their fluid balance.

Conversions

6. A healthy person generally needs to take in about 64 ounces (oz) of fluid each day.

   How many milliliters (mL) is this?
   _____ mL

   How many cups is this?
   _____ cups

7. Mrs. Wyant drinks half of a glass of orange juice. The glass holds about 1 cup of liquid.

   How many milliliters of orange juice did Mrs. Wyant drink?
   _____ mL

8. Mr. Ramirez just ate some chocolate pudding from a 6-ounce container. The leftover pudding is measured and is about 35 mL.

   How many milliliters of pudding did Mr. Ramirez eat?
   _____ mL

9. Miss Sumiko has a bowl of soup for lunch. The soup bowl holds about 1½ cups of liquid.

   How many milliliters (mL) is this?
   _____ mL

   Miss Sumiko finishes most of her soup, but there are about 25 mL left.

   How many mL of soup did Miss Sumiko eat?
   _____ mL

Short Answer

10. List three guidelines that a home health aide should follow when a client vomits.

_____

_____

_____

_____

_____

_____

Name: _____

4. Describe the guidelines for catheter care

Matching
Use each letter only once.

1. _____ Catheter

2. _____ Condom catheter

3. _____ Indwelling catheter

4. _____ Straight catheter

5. _____ Urinary catheter

(A) Urinary catheter that has an attachment that fits onto the penis

(B) Urinary catheter that is removed immediately after urine is drained

(C) Thin tube used to drain urine from the bladder

(D) Urinary catheter that stays inside the bladder for a period of time

(E) Thin tube inserted into the body that is used to drain or inject fluids

True or False

6. _____ The drainage bag for a urinary catheter must always be kept lower than the bladder or hips.

7. _____ For clients who have urinary catheters, daily care of the genital area is important to avoid infection.

8. _____ The home health aide is responsible for removing a urinary catheter once the doctor says it is no longer needed.

9. _____ When cleaning the area near the catheter, the home health aide should use a clean area of the washcloth for each stroke.

5. Explain the benefits of warm and cold applications

Crossword
Across

3. Cold applications can bring down this

4. Type of application that helps stop bleeding

6. A warm soak of the perineal area to clean perineal wounds and reduce pain

Down

1. A condition that could cause a person to be unable to feel or notice damage is occurring from a warm or cold application

2. Numbness, pain, blisters, and skin that is this color should be reported to the supervisor

5. Type of application that increases blood flow to an injured area

Multiple Choice

7. Which of the following is a type of dry warm application?
   (A) Cold compress
   (B) Warm tub bath
   (C) Warm soak
   (D) Disposable warm pack

8. Heat relieves pain by
   (A) Increasing blood flow to the area
   (B) Decreasing oxygen to the tissues
   (C) Bringing down high fevers
   (D) Causing numbness in the area

9. Which of the following is a type of moist cold application?
   (A) Warm sitz bath
   (B) Warm compress
   (C) Disposable cold pack
   (D) Ice pack

10. What is the proper water temperature when making a warm compress?
    (A) No higher than 95 degrees Fahrenheit
    (B) No higher than 105 degrees Fahrenheit
    (C) No higher than 120 degrees Fahrenheit
    (D) No higher than 125 degrees Fahrenheit

6. Explain how to apply non-sterile dressings

Short Answer

What is the difference between sterile and non-sterile dressings?

_____

_____

_____

_____

_____

_____

_____

_____

7. Describe the purpose of elastic stockings and how to apply them

Multiple Choice

1. Why are elastic stockings ordered for some clients?
   (A) They help prevent diabetes.
   (B) They help prevent anemia.
   (C) They help prevent blood clots.
   (D) They help prevent chronic obstructive pulmonary disease.

2. The best time to apply elastic stockings is
   (A) In the evening, before the client goes to bed
   (B) In the morning, before the client gets out of bed
   (C) In the early afternoon, before the client gets back in bed to rest
   (D) In the late morning, before the client has lunch

3. Where should the heel of the stocking be after the stocking is applied?
   (A) Over the client's toes
   (B) Over the client's heel
   (C) Over the client's lower calf
   (D) Over the client's shin

8. Define *ostomy* and list care guidelines

True or False

1. _____ An ostomy is the surgical creation of an opening from an area inside the body to the outside.

2. _____ The artificial opening in the abdomen through which stool is eliminated is called a stoma.

3. _____ Clients who have ileostomies will need to restrict their fluid intake.

4. _____ The home health aide should wear gloves when providing ostomy care.

Short Answer

5. Why might a client be embarrassed by his ostomy?

_____

_____

_____

_____

_____

_____

_____

_____

Multiple Choice

6. How often should an ostomy pouch be emptied and cleaned or replaced?
   (A) Once a day
   (B) Every hour
   (C) Whenever a stool is eliminated
   (D) Before a client gets out of bed for the day

7. What could cause a food blockage in a client who has an ileostomy?
   (A) Too much liquid in the client's diet
   (B) A large amount of high-fiber food in the client's diet
   (C) Skin irritation
   (D) Cold compresses

9. Describe how to assist with an elastic bandage

Multiple Choice

1. Elastic bandages are also known as
    (A) Non-sterile bandages
    (B) Plastic bandages
    (C) Liquid bandages
    (D) Aseptic bandages

2. One purpose of elastic bandages is to
    (A) Elevate a cast
    (B) Hold a dressing in place
    (C) Cover pressure injuries
    (D) Help with ambulation

3. Elastic bandages should be applied snugly enough to control _____ and prevent movement of _____.
    (A) Temperature, the client
    (B) Bleeding, dressings
    (C) Elevation, dressings
    (D) Movement, temperature

4. How soon should the home health aide check on a client after applying a bandage?
    (A) 60 minutes
    (B) 30 minutes
    (C) 2 hours
    (D) 10 minutes

15

Medications and Technology in Home Care

1. List four guidelines for safe and proper use of medications

True or False

1. ____ Home health aides must not handle or give medications unless specifically trained and assigned to do so.

2. ____ Home health aides are not allowed to touch the client's medication containers in any way.

3. ____ It is not important for the home health aide to know what medications the client is taking, as long as the HHA documents when they are taken.

4. ____ Home health aides should report symptoms such as stomachache or vomiting because these could indicate a side effect or drug interaction.

5. ____ Aspirin and ibuprofen are examples of over-the-counter drugs.

2. Identify the five "rights" of medications

Multiple Choice

1. Checking the label for instructions on how the medication should be taken is which right of medication?
   (A) The Right Client
   (B) The Right Route
   (C) The Right Time
   (D) The Right Medication

2. Checking the label for instructions on how much medication to take is which right of medication?
   (A) The Right Amount
   (B) The Right Client
   (C) The Right Time
   (D) The Right Route

3. Making sure the medication name on the container matches the name listed in the care plan is which right of medication?
   (A) The Right Time
   (B) The Right Medication
   (C) The Right Client
   (D) The Right Amount

4. Checking the label to make sure the client's name is on it is which right of medication?
   (A) The Right Client
   (B) The Right Medication
   (C) The Right Time
   (D) The Right Route

5. Checking the label for instructions on how often the medication should be taken is which right of medication?
   (A) The Right Route
   (B) The Right Client
   (C) The Right Time
   (D) The Right Amount

3. Explain how to assist a client with self-administered medications

True or False

1. ____ All medications should be taken with food to avoid stomach irritation.

2. _____ To avoid any problems with drug interactions, the home health aide should document every medication the client takes, whether it is part of the treatment plan or not.

3. _____ Sedatives should never be mixed with alcohol.

4. _____ The home health aide can remind a client when it is time to take medication.

5. _____ Allergic reactions to medication may require emergency help.

Short Answer

6. List seven ways in which home health aides may help clients with self-medication.

_____

_____

_____

_____

_____

_____

_____

_____

_____

_____

_____

_____

7. List ten actions involving self-medication that home health aides are NOT allowed to do.

_____

_____

_____

_____

_____

_____

_____

_____

_____

_____

_____

8. Name five common side effects that clients may experience from their medications.

_____

_____

_____

_____

_____

_____

_____

4. Identify observations about medications that should be reported right away

Short Answer

1. What should the home health aide do if a client shows signs of a reaction to a medication or complains of side effects?

_____

_____

2. What should the home health aide do if a client takes medication in the wrong amount, at the wrong time, or takes the wrong kind of medication?

_____

_____

5. Describe what to do in an emergency involving medications

Short Answer

1. Mrs. Mallory takes several prescription medications each day as ordered by her physician. On the day her home health aide (HHA) is scheduled to visit her, the HHA arrives at her home to find Mrs. Mallory sitting down in a chair and looking very ill. When the HHA asks her if she is okay, Mrs. Mallory says that she feels very sick to her stomach and she thinks she might faint. Mrs. Mallory says that she might have taken too much medication because she could not remember if she had already taken her morning dosage. What would be the best response by the HHA?

_____
_____
_____
_____
_____
_____
_____
_____
_____

2. The home health aide arrives at Mr. MacIntyre's home at 8:30 a.m. and finds him lying in bed. The HHA is unable to wake him, and then she notices several bottles of pills on the table next to the bed. They are all open, and some of the pills are scattered on the table and the floor. What would be the best response by the HHA?

_____
_____
_____
_____
_____

_____
_____
_____
_____
_____

6. Identify methods of medication storage

True or False

1. ____ The client's medication should be kept separate from medicine used by other members of the household.

2. ____ If young children are present in the home, medications should be stored on top of the counter.

3. ____ Medications should be stored away from heat and light.

4. ____ If medication has expired, the home health aide should discard it in the trash.

7. Identify signs of drug misuse and abuse and know how to report these

Multiple Choice

1. Proper medication usage includes which of the following?
(A) Refusing to take medications
(B) Taking medication with alcohol
(C) Sharing medication with others
(D) Taking the right dose at the right time

2. The best thing the home health aide can do if a client refuses to take medication is to
(A) Push the client to take the medication, explaining that it is good for him
(B) Try to find out why the client does not want to take the medication and report to the supervisor
(C) Call 911 for emergency medical help
(D) Call the client's doctor immediately

Name: _____

3. A common reason why people avoid taking prescribed medication is
   (A) They dislike the side effects
   (B) They are stubborn
   (C) They do not want to feel better
   (D) They would rather get well without it

4. Signs of drug misuse or abuse include
   (A) Increased appetite and weight gain
   (B) Unusual cheerfulness
   (C) Depression and moodiness
   (D) Better relationships with family members

5. The drugs that pose the highest risk for causing drug dependency are
   (A) Pain medications
   (B) Antihistamines (allergy medicines)
   (C) Beta blockers
   (D) Multivitamins

8. Demonstrate an understanding of oxygen equipment

True or False

1. _____ Oxygen therapy is the administration of oxygen to increase the supply of oxygen to the lungs.

2. _____ Oxygen is prescribed by a doctor.

3. _____ Home health aides are usually responsible for adjusting oxygen settings for clients.

4. _____ Oxygen supports combustion; this means it makes other things burn.

5. _____ A flammable liquid like alcohol is fine to have in a room when oxygen is in use, as long as it is covered.

6. _____ It is all right to smoke in a room where oxygen is stored as long as the oxygen is not in use.

7. _____ Oxygen should be turned off in the event of a fire.

8. _____ It is important for the home health aide to check the skin around oxygen masks and tubing for irritation.

9. _____ If a client has skin irritation around a nasal cannula, the HHA should use Vaseline to soften the skin.

Multiple Choice

10. Which of the following is a box-like device that changes air in the room into air with more oxygen?
    (A) Oxygen cannula
    (B) Oxygen face mask
    (C) Oxygen concentrator
    (D) Oxygen prongs

11. Who is responsible for servicing oxygen tanks or concentrators in a client's home?
    (A) The doctor who prescribed the oxygen
    (B) The home health aide
    (C) The client's family members
    (D) The agency that supplies the oxygen

12. When should the home health aide administer a client's oxygen?
    (A) Whenever the client requests that she do so
    (B) Every three days
    (C) According to the care plan
    (D) Never

13. Which of the following can liquid oxygen cause?
    (A) Frostbite
    (B) Addiction
    (C) Digestive problems
    (D) Congestive heart failure

14. What kind of water is used in humidifying bottles for oxygen concentrators?
    (A) Sparkling water
    (B) Natural spring water
    (C) Sterile water
    (D) Tap water

15. What is the purpose of a humidifier?
    (A) To put only warm moisture in the air
    (B) To remove moisture from the air
    (C) To put warm or cool moisture in the air
    (D) To clean the air without adding moisture

9. Explain care guidelines for intravenous (IV) therapy

Multiple Choice

1. IVs allow direct access to
   (A) The heart
   (B) The lungs
   (C) The bloodstream
   (D) The muscles

2. What is the home health aide's responsibility for IV care?
   (A) Inserting IV lines
   (B) Removing IV lines
   (C) Care of the IV site
   (D) Documenting and reporting observations

3. Which of the following refers to treatments that are used in addition to the conventional treatments prescribed by a doctor?
   (A) Western medicine
   (B) Complementary medicine
   (C) Oxygen therapy
   (D) Respiratory medicine

4. Treating a person with acupuncture means
   (A) Putting the hands on both sides of the spine to realign it
   (B) Taking tablets that contain a specific healing substance
   (C) Using targeted laser light on specific body parts
   (D) Inserting very fine needles into points on the body

Name: _____

Medications and Technology in Home Care

16
Rehabilitation and Restorative Care

1. Discuss rehabilitation and restorative care

Short Answer

1. List four goals of a rehabilitative program.

_____

_____

_____

_____

_____

2. What is the goal of restorative care?

_____

_____

_____

_____

_____

2. Explain the home care rehabilitation model

Short Answer

List five members of the team who may participate in a client's restorative care.

_____

_____

_____

_____

_____

3. Describe guidelines for assisting with rehabilitation and restorative care

True or False

1. _____ The HHA should ignore any setbacks a client experiences so she does not become discouraged.

2. _____ All clients will enjoy being encouraged in an obvious way.

3. _____ The home health aide should do everything for the client, rather than having him try to do it himself. Doing this will help speed recovery.

4. _____ The HHA should not report any decline in a client's ability, because all clients in restorative care will have a decline in ability.

5. _____ Family members and clients will take cues from the home health aide on how to behave.

6. _____ Tasks should be broken down into small steps.

7. _____ It is important for the home health aide to report any signs of depression or mood changes in a client.

4. Describe how to assist with range of motion exercises

Labeling
For the following illustrations, write the correct term for each body movement.

1. _____

Rehabilitation and Restorative Care

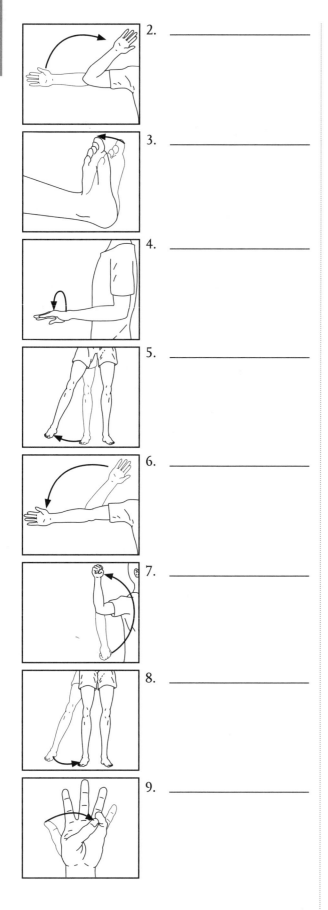

2. _____

3. _____

4. _____

5. _____

6. _____

7. _____

8. _____

9. _____

Multiple Choice

10. In what order should the HHA perform range of motion (ROM) exercises?
    (A) He should start from the feet and work upward.
    (B) He should start from the shoulders and work downward.
    (C) He should start at the hands and work inward.
    (D) He should exercise the arms last.

11. If a client reports pain during ROM exercises, the home health aide should
    (A) Continue with the exercises as planned
    (B) Continue, but perform the motion that caused pain more gently
    (C) Stop the exercises and report the pain to his supervisor
    (D) Stop the motion for one minute before starting again

12. How many times should each ROM exercise be repeated?
    (A) At least 6 times
    (B) At least 10 times
    (C) At least 12 times
    (D) At least 3 times

5. Explain guidelines for maintaining proper body alignment

Fill in the Blank

1. Observe principles of body _____. Remember that proper alignment is based on straight _____. _____ or rolled or folded _____ may be needed to support the small of the back and raise the knees or head in the supine position.

2. Keep body parts in natural _____. In a natural hand position, the fingers are slightly _____. Use _____ to keep covers from resting on feet for clients in the supine position.

3. Prevent external rotation of
    _____. Change
    _____ frequently
    to prevent muscle stiffness and pressure
    injuries. This should be done at least every
    _____ hours.

6. List guidelines for providing basic skin care and preventing pressure injuries

Crossword

Across

1. The bottom sheet on a client's bed must be
    kept tight and free from _____.

4. Skin should be kept clean and ____.

5. One type of material that prevents air from
    circulating, causing the skin to sweat

7. Skin this color should not be massaged

Down

2. A problem that can result from pulling a cli-
    ent across the sheet when transferring him

3. Keeps top sheets from resting on the legs
    and feet

6. At a minimum, the number of hours at
    which immobile clients should be
    repositioned

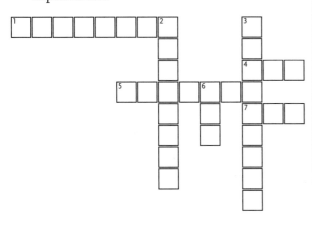

7. Describe the guidelines for caring for clients who have fractures or casts

Multiple Choice

1. When caring for a client who has a cast,
    _____ the extremity that is
    in a cast to help stop swelling.
    (A) Lower
    (B) Double bandage
    (C) Elevate
    (D) Shake

2. Keep the cast _____ at all times.
    (A) Dry
    (B) Wet
    (C) Hot
    (D) Pointed

3. Osteoporosis occurs more frequently in
    _____ people.
    (A) Young
    (B) Active
    (C) Elderly
    (D) Diabetic

4. Signs and symptoms of a fracture include
    (A) Moistness at the site
    (B) Cold area at the site
    (C) Swelling at the site
    (D) Dryness at the site

5. Fractures are broken bones and may be
    caused by
    (A) Excessive fiber
    (B) Asthma
    (C) Osteoporosis
    (D) Too much progesterone

6. Casts that are made of fiberglass are
    (A) Heavy
    (B) Unable to dry properly
    (C) Lightweight
    (D) Less reliable than other types of casts

7. When should a client insert something
    inside the cast?
    (A) When skin itches
    (B) After the cast dries
    (C) When the cast is wet
    (D) Never

8. List the guidelines for caring for clients who have had a hip replacement

True or False

1. _____ Most fractured hips require surgery.

2. _____ The home health aide should perform range of motion exercises on the operative leg to help with healing.

3. _____ Preventing falls is an important part of preventing hip fractures.

4. _____ Elderly people heal slowly.

5. _____ Home health aides may disconnect a traction assembly if the client requests it.

6. _____ When transferring a client from the bed, a pillow should be used between the thighs to keep the legs separated.

7. _____ The home health aide should begin with the unaffected, or stronger, side first when dressing a client who is recovering from a hip replacement.

8. _____ The stronger side always leads in standing, pivoting, and sitting.

Multiple Choice

9. Which side should clients recovering from hip replacements dress first?
   (A) Affected/weaker side
   (B) Right side
   (C) Unaffected/stronger side
   (D) Left side

10. What does the abbreviation *PWB* stand for?
    (A) Previously-weakened bones
    (B) Partial weight-bearing
    (C) Patient's weight before
    (D) Patient wants baths

11. If a home health aide sees *NWB* on a client's care plan, the client
    (A) Can support 100 percent of his body weight on a step
    (B) Can support some weight, but not all, on one or both legs
    (C) Is unable to support any weight on one or both legs
    (D) Can use stairs without assistance

9. List ways to adapt the environment for people with physical limitations

Short Answer

Choose an adaptive device from Figure 16-27 in the textbook (one you did not choose to answer question 14 in the Chapter Review). Describe how it might help a client who is recovering from or adapting to a physical condition.

_____

_____

_____

_____

_____

_____

_____

_____

_____

_____

_____

10. Identify reasons clients lose bowel or bladder control

Fill in the Blank

1. When people cannot control the muscles of the bowel or bladder, they are said to be _____.

2. A(n) _____ placed on the bed helps protect the bed.

3. Clients who are incontinent need to be kept _____, _____, and free from odor.

4. Home health aides should offer clients who are incontinent a _____ or take them to the bathroom before beginning long procedures.

5. Urine and feces need to be washed off completely by bathing and proper _____ care.

6. Home health aides should not refer to incontinence briefs or pads as

_____

because clients are not infants.

7. Clients who are incontinent need

_____, under-standing, and empathy from home health aides.

11. Explain the guidelines for assisting with bowel or bladder retraining

Scenarios

Ms. Potter has been recovering from a broken hip. Her recovery is proceeding well, but she has had a problem with urinary incontinence since her injury. Her doctor asked that bladder retraining be added into her care plan. Below are examples of how three home health aides (HHAs) help Ms. Potter with retraining. Read each one and state what the HHA is doing well and/or what he or she should do differently.

1. Hannah, a new HHA, wants to be very pro-fessional about the episodes of incontinence. While she is cleaning the bed, she remains very upbeat and friendly and does not men-tion the incontinence unless Ms. Potter brings it up.

_____

_____

_____

_____

2. Greta senses Ms. Potter's acute embarrass-ment, and it makes her nervous. Whenever she has to assist Ms. Potter with retraining efforts, she speaks very little and does not make eye contact with her. She tries to finish her work as quickly as possible to limit Ms. Potter's discomfort.

_____

_____

_____

_____

3. Pete has been very encouraging and positive with Ms. Potter. He has charted her bath-room schedule. He encourages her to drink more fluids. He makes sure he is nearby to help her during the usual times that she needs to go to the bathroom.

_____

_____

_____

_____

_____

12. Describe the benefits of deep breathing exercises

Short Answer

What can deep breathing exercises help?

_____

_____

_____

_____

_____

_____

_____

Name: _____

17
Clients with Disabilities

1. Identify common causes of disabilities

Short Answer

1. List three factors that affect how well a person copes with a disability.

_____

_____

_____

_____

_____

2. List six diseases and disorders that may cause disability.

_____

_____

_____

_____

_____

_____

3. What are two types of disabilities that can be caused by injury to the head or spinal cord?

_____

_____

_____

2. Describe daily challenges a person with a disability may face

Short Answer

List five daily challenges a person with a disability may face.

_____

_____

_____

_____

_____

_____

_____

_____

3. Define terms related to disabilities and explain why they are important

Short Answer

1. What are some terms you use to define yourself (e.g., race, sexual orientation, religion, political affiliation)?

_____

_____

_____

_____

_____

2. List a few terms that might be more preferable to people with disabilities.

_____

_____

_____

_____

_____

_____

Name: _____

4. Identify social and emotional needs of persons with disabilities

Fill in the Blank

1. Basic psychosocial needs include independence, social interaction, acceptance, a sense of worth, and
    _____.

2. Home health aides should treat all clients with
    _____.

3. Home health aides should not push clients beyond their
    _____.

4. Home health aides can give clients
    _____ to show what they can do by themselves.

5. Explain how a disability may affect sexuality and intimacy

True or False

1. _____ A disabled person does not generally experience sexual desires.

2. _____ For disabled people, the ability to meet sexual needs may be limited.

3. _____ People in wheelchairs are unable to have sexual relationships.

4. _____ It is important for home health aides not to judge any sexual behavior they see.

6. Identify skills that can be applied to clients with disabilities

Short Answer

List three skills that can be applied to working with clients with disabilities.

_____

_____

_____

_____

7. List five goals to work toward when assisting clients who have disabilities

Fill in the Blank

1. Promote self-care and
    _____.

2. Assure the client's
    _____.

3. Promote the client's health and
    _____.

4. Maintain the client's
    _____ and self-worth.

5. Maintain the _____ of the client's household.

8. Identify five qualities of excellent service needed by clients with disabilities

Short Answer

List the five qualities of excellent service needed by clients with disabilities.

_____

_____

_____

_____

_____

_____

_____

9. Explain how to adapt personal care procedures to meet the needs of clients with disabilities

True or False

1. _____ Children who have Down syndrome do not appear physically different from any other child.

2. _____ Developmental disabilities normally appear and are diagnosed when a person is middle-aged.

3. ____ The most common type of developmental disorder is an intellectual disability.

4. ____ Having an intellectual disability is the same as having a mental illness.

5. ____ Clients who have an intellectual disability have the same emotional and physical needs that others have.

6. ____ Speech impairment is one effect of cerebral palsy.

7. ____ It is possible that some babies born with spina bifida will be able to walk and experience no lasting disabilities.

8. ____ One sign of autism spectrum disorder is that the child does not engage in pretend play.

9. ____ An inability to be empathetic is one problem that autism spectrum disorder causes.

10. ____ Ideally treatment for autism spectrum disorder should be started early and tailored to the individual.

10. List important changes to report and document for a client with disabilities

Short Answer

1. What should the home health aide do if he notices that a client is unable to perform a task that she was previously able to do?

_____

_____

_____

_____

2. Give two signs of depression that should be reported.

_____

_____

_____

_____

Name: _____

18
Mental Health and Mental Illness

1. Identify seven characteristics of mental health

Short Answer

1. Define mental health.

_____

_____

_____

_____

_____

_____

2. List seven characteristics of a person who is mentally healthy.

_____

_____

_____

_____

_____

_____

_____

_____

_____

_____

2. Identify four causes of mental illness

True or False

1. _____ Signs and symptoms of mental illness include confusion, disorientation, agitation, and anxiety.

2. _____ A situation response may be triggered by severe changes in the environment.

3. _____ A person who is mentally healthy cannot experience a situation response.

4. _____ Mental illness can be caused by substance abuse or a chemical imbalance.

5. _____ The building blocks of mental health are self-respect and self-worth.

6. _____ Traumatic experiences early in life do not cause mental illness.

7. _____ Mental illness cannot be inherited.

8. _____ Extreme stress may result in mental illness.

3. Distinguish between fact and fallacy concerning mental illness

True or False

1. _____ A fallacy is a false belief.

2. _____ People who are mentally ill have the power to control their illness if they really want to.

3. _____ People who are mentally ill usually do not want to get well.

4. _____ Mental illness is a disorder just like any physical illness.

5. _____ People who are mentally ill often cannot control their emotions or responses.

6. _____ An intellectual disability is a type of mental illness.

Name: _____

4. Explain the connection between mental and physical wellness

Short Answer

Briefly describe why mental health is important to physical health.

_____

_____

_____

_____

_____

_____

5. List guidelines for communicating with clients who are mentally ill

Short Answer

1. When communicating with a client who has a mental illness, why is it important for the home health aide to treat the client as an individual and to tailor the HHA's style of communication to the situation?

_____

_____

_____

_____

_____

_____

2. Why is it important for the home health aide not to talk to adults as if they were children?

_____

_____

_____

_____

_____

6. Identify and define common defense mechanisms

Short Answer
Read each description below and identify the defense mechanism that is being used.

1. When Aaron's mother yells at him for breaking a vase in the living room, he goes into his room and yells at his stuffed bear.

_____

2. When Gia was 10, she was very badly injured in a car accident. She was in the hospital for almost three months, but now she tries not to think about that time.

_____

3. When Mark accuses his little sister Sarah of having a crush on the boy who sits next to her in class, she blushes and cries, "I do not!"

_____

4. When Esther was 42, her husband died of lung cancer. After his death, she got out the quilt she used to sleep with as a child and curled up in bed with it for days.

_____

5. Wayne is fixing a leaky sink in the bathroom. When his wife teases him about taking a long time to fix it, he replies, "It's not my fault. I can't concentrate on anything with you bothering me all the time."

_____

7. Describe anxiety, depression, and schizophrenia

Multiple Choice

1. Uneasiness, worry, or fear, often about a situation or condition, is called
   (A) Anxiety
   (B) Withdrawal
   (C) Fatigue
   (D) Apathy

2. An intense, irrational fear of an object, place, or situation is called a(n)
(A) Depressive episode
(B) Delusion
(C) Phobia
(D) Hallucination

3. Which type of mental illness is most commonly associated with suicide in older adults?
(A) Anxiety
(B) Apathy
(C) Irritability
(D) Depression

4. Which of the following means a lack of interest in activities?
(A) Guilt
(B) Depression
(C) Apathy
(D) Delusion

5. A persistent false belief, such as a person believing that someone else is controlling his thoughts, is a
(A) Defense mechanism
(B) Delusion
(C) Phobia
(D) Hallucination

6. An anxiety disorder that is characterized by obsessive thoughts causing a person to repeatedly perform a behavior is called
(A) Generalized anxiety disorder
(B) Posttraumatic stress disorder
(C) Obsessive-compulsive disorder
(D) Panic disorder

8. Explain common treatments for mental illness

True or False

1. ____ Mental illness cannot be treated.

2. ____ Medication and psychotherapy are commonly used to treat mental illness.

3. ____ Home health aides are responsible for prescribing medication for clients who are mentally ill.

4. ____ Medication can allow those who are mentally ill to function more completely.

9. Explain the home health aide's role in caring for clients who are mentally ill

Short Answer

List four guidelines for home health aides who are caring for clients who are mentally ill.

_____

_____

_____

_____

_____

_____

10. Identify important observations that should be made and reported

True or False

1. ____ It is important for the home health aide to report to the supervisor if a client who is mentally ill stops taking her medication.

2. ____ As long as a client is joking when talking about suicide, the home health aide does not need to report it.

11. List the signs of substance abuse

Multiple Choice

1. Circle any of the following substances that can be abused:
(A) Alcohol
(B) Cigarettes
(C) Decongestants
(D) Diet aids
(E) Illegal drugs
(F) Glue
(G) Paint
(H) Prescription medicine

2. A client has been acting a little strangely lately. She gets upset very easily and her eyes are always red. She does not eat much, and sometimes her home health aide can smell alcohol on her breath, even in the morning. What is the best response by the HHA?

(A) Confront the client about what the HHA has noticed

(B) Contact Alcoholics Anonymous to get advice on how to handle the situation

(C) Document the HHA's observations and report them to her supervisor

(D) Search the client's cabinets for alcohol and throw away any alcohol found

19

New Mothers, Infants, and Children

1. Explain the growth of home care for new mothers and infants

True or False

1. _____ Most new mothers stay in the hospital for several days to a week after childbirth.

2. _____ Bed rest is ordered if a woman shows signs of early labor.

3. _____ Home health aides may be needed when an expectant mother is put on bed rest by her doctor.

4. _____ New mothers today are generally more energetic when they come home than women in the past.

5. _____ Bed rest may help prevent labor from starting before the baby is ready to be born.

6. _____ Natural childbirth has been increasing in popularity.

2. Identify common neonatal disorders

Short Answer

List three common neonatal disorders.

_____

_____

_____

_____

_____

3. Explain how to provide postpartum care

Fill in the Blank
Use this list of words and phrases to fill in the blanks in the following sentences.

bathing	Cesarean section
diapering	episiotomy
feeding	housekeeping
lactation	lochia
monitor	pink
red	

1. An incision sometimes made in the perineal area during vaginal delivery to enlarge the vaginal opening for the baby's head is a(n)

   _____.

2. The home health aide may need to monitor the amount and color of the new mother's

   _____,

   which is the vaginal flow that occurs after giving birth.

3. Basic care for the baby includes

   _____,

   _____, and

   _____.

4. The home health aide may be required to do light _____ to help the new mother.

5. A surgical procedure in which the baby is delivered through an incision in the mother's abdomen is called a

   _____.

Name: _____

6. Home health aides may be asked to
_____ the
equipment if the baby is receiving oxygen.

7. During the first several days, the color
of lochia usually changes from bright
_____ to _____.

8. If a new mother needs help with breastfeeding, a _____
consultant can help.

4. List important observations to report and document

Short Answer
Read this scenario and answer the questions that follow.

The home health aide (HHA) arrives at a client's house at 8 a.m. to care for baby Eric, a two-day-old newborn, and finds the house dirty, the new mother Anne in a sitz bath, and baby Eric in the crib crying. The mother is also crying and complains of getting "no sleep last night." What course of action should the HHA take? How would the HHA document this?

_____
_____
_____
_____
_____
_____
_____
_____
_____
_____
_____
_____
_____
_____
_____

5. Explain guidelines for safely handling a baby

Labeling
Label the type of hold shown in each figure.

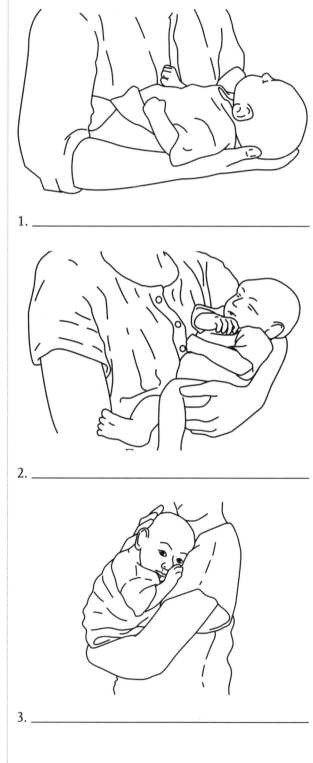

1. _____

2. _____

3. _____

6. Describe guidelines for assisting with feeding a baby

Multiple Choice

1. If the baby does not latch onto the nipple right away, the mother should stroke his
   (A) Toes
   (B) Elbows
   (C) Cheek
   (D) Forehead

2. Many professionals recommend that mothers try breastfeeding for _____ week(s) before deciding whether to continue or stop.
   (A) Five
   (B) Ten
   (C) One
   (D) Two

3. Powdered formula is sold in
   (A) Crates
   (B) Cans
   (C) Sterilized pitchers
   (D) Covered plastic bowls

4. The cheapest formula is usually
   (A) Ready-to-use
   (B) Concentrated liquid
   (C) Powdered
   (D) Ready-made

5. A good position for breastfeeding is
   (A) Lying face down on the bed
   (B) Sitting upright in a comfortable chair
   (C) Rocking rapidly in a chair
   (D) Bending over the crib

6. Before feeding, the home health aide should check the temperature of the formula on her wrist. It should feel
   (A) Warm
   (B) Hot
   (C) Cold
   (D) Boiling

7. The mother can break the suction of a nursing baby by
   (A) Pulling down the baby's ears
   (B) Putting her finger in the baby's mouth
   (C) Sucking on the baby's toes
   (D) Shaking the baby

8. Which of the following is best for bottle-fed newborns?
   (A) Whole milk
   (B) Infant formula
   (C) Fruit smoothies
   (D) Skim milk

7. Explain guidelines for bathing and changing a baby

True or False

1. ____ The home health aide should wear disposable gloves when changing or bathing a baby.

2. ____ Leaving a diaper off for a few minutes when changing the baby can help prevent diaper rash.

3. ____ The proper way to test a baby's bath temperature is by dipping the baby's hand in it.

4. ____ Moisture contributes to diaper rash.

5. ____ It is okay for the home health aide to take both hands off the baby if it is for less than a minute.

6. ____ Children generally wear diapers until they are 8 to 12 months old.

7. ____ Newborns will need between eight and 12 diaper changes in 24 hours.

8. ____ The home health aide should always apply baby powder after giving a baby a bath.

9. ____ It is a sign of a medical problem if a newborn baby has a loose bowel movement with every feeding.

10. ____ Babies should be changed frequently to avoid diaper rash.

8. Identify how to measure weight and length of a baby

Multiple Choice

1. When weighing a baby, the home health aide should
    (A) Keep one hand on the baby at all times
    (B) Step back from the scale after the baby is on it
    (C) Place the scale on the floor to see if the baby will crawl onto it
    (D) Stand the baby up on the scale for an accurate weight

2. How can a baby's length be determined?
    (A) By standing the baby up against a wall, making a pencil mark at the top of his head, and measuring the height of the mark
    (B) By holding the baby against the home health aide's leg and measuring how high the baby's head reaches
    (C) By placing the baby on paper, making pencil marks at the head and heel, and measuring the distance between the marks
    (D) By putting the baby on a standing scale and lowering the measuring rod until it rests flat on the baby's head

9. Explain guidelines for special care

Matching

1. _____ Apnea

2. _____ Circumcision

3. _____ Oxygen

4. _____ Umbilical cord

(A) The cord that connects the baby to the placenta

(B) The removal of part of the foreskin of the penis

(C) The state of not breathing

(D) Given to some babies who have breathing problems; considered a medication

10. Identify special needs of children and describe how children respond to stress

Short Answer

1. List some examples of physical needs that children have.

    _____

    _____

    _____

    _____

    _____

    _____

2. List an example of a mental need that children have.

    _____

    _____

    _____

3. List four examples of emotional needs that children have.

    _____

    _____

    _____

    _____

    _____

    _____

    _____

4. List five reasons that children may experience stress.

    _____

    _____

    _____

    _____

    _____

    _____

5. List five factors that influence the way in which children respond to stress.

_____

_____

_____

_____

_____

_____

_____

6. In what ways might school-age children react to stress?

_____

_____

_____

_____

_____

_____

_____

7. In what negative ways might adolescents react to stress?

_____

_____

_____

_____

_____

_____

_____

11. List symptoms of common childhood illnesses and the required care

Fill in the Blank

1. _____, cleaning, and disinfection are the best ways to prevent infection.

2. Frequent loose or watery bowel movements are called _____.

3. Children with diarrhea may experience _____, thus doctors may recommend electrolyte-replacement drinks.

4. In general, children should not be given _____, because it has been associated with some serious disorders.

5. Treatment of a fever includes a luke-warm bath or acetaminophen or _____.

6. When children have diarrhea, doctors usually recommend that they resume their normal, well-balanced diet within _____ hours of getting sick.

7. Rest and _____ are recommended for fevers.

8. Too much acetaminophen can cause _____ damage.

12. Identify guidelines for working with children

Scenarios

Read the following scenarios and decide how to respond.

1. Zack and his older brother Lee have just returned home from school. Zack is upset because he did not win a prize for his science project, but his brother did. He cried at school, and some of the other kids made fun of him. He becomes visibly distressed again as he relates this story to the home health aide at his home. What would be the best response by the home health aide?

_____

_____

_____

_____

_____

_____

_____

_____

_____

_____

_____

2. The home health aide notices that Doug has been withdrawn all afternoon. He did not go outside to play after school, and at dinner, he refuses to eat anything. He makes comments like "nobody cares about me." What would be the best response by the home health aide?

_____

_____

_____

_____

_____

_____

_____

_____

_____

_____

13. List the signs of child abuse and neglect and know how to report them

Short Answer

1. Psychological abuse of children includes

_____

_____

_____

_____

_____

2. Sexual abuse of children includes

_____

_____

_____

3. Child neglect is

_____

_____

_____

_____

20

Dying, Death, and Hospice

1. Discuss the stages of grief

Multiple Choice

Read each scenario below and choose which stage of grief the person described is experiencing.

1. Mr. Cane was told two years ago that a tumor in his brain was inoperable and would eventually be fatal. Since that time, he has visited many specialists. Despite receiving the same diagnosis from every doctor, he continues to seek further opinions, insisting that each doctor try to remove the tumor. Which stage of grief is Mr. Cane in?
    (A) Denial
    (B) Anger
    (C) Bargaining
    (D) Depression
    (E) Acceptance

2. Mrs. Tyler is dying of heart disease. One day as her home health aide, Annie, is assisting her with personal care, Mrs. Tyler lashes out at her. She tells Annie that she is a dumb girl who is wasting her life and does not deserve the many years she has left to live. Which stage of grief is Mrs. Tyler in?
    (A) Denial
    (B) Anger
    (C) Bargaining
    (D) Depression
    (E) Acceptance

3. Mr. Lopez is dying of AIDS. He has called all of his friends to say goodbye and has discussed at length with his family the kind of memorial service he would like them to arrange. What stage of grief is Mr. Lopez in?
    (A) Denial
    (B) Anger
    (C) Bargaining
    (D) Depression
    (E) Acceptance

4. Ms. Corke has always been lively and happy. Since she learned that she has Lou Gehrig's disease, however, her mood has changed drastically. Although she is still healthy enough to do activities, she rarely leaves her bedroom or even changes out of her pajamas. Which stage of grief is Ms. Corke in?
    (A) Denial
    (B) Anger
    (C) Bargaining
    (D) Depression
    (E) Acceptance

5. Mr. Celasco has had lung cancer for several years. During that time, he has tried to quit smoking but has been unsuccessful. When he finds out that there are no further treatments for him to try, he pledges that he will give up smoking in exchange for a few more years of life. What stage of grief is Mr. Celasco in?
    (A) Denial
    (B) Anger
    (C) Bargaining
    (D) Depression
    (E) Acceptance

2. Describe the grief process

Multiple Choice

Read each scenario below and choose which reaction to a loved one's death each person is experiencing.

1. Malcolm's wife died during the birth of their second daughter. Malcolm is so upset with her for abandoning him and the children that he cannot even stand to hear her name spoken. What reaction is Malcolm experiencing?
   (A) Loneliness
   (B) Denial
   (C) Anger
   (D) Guilt
   (E) Sadness

2. Becky's mother had been ill for many years before she died when Becky was 15 years old. After her death, Becky remembers how she used to resent helping her mother around the house so much and wishes that she had been kinder and more cheerful. Which reaction is she having?
   (A) Anger
   (B) Sadness
   (C) Guilt
   (D) Denial
   (E) Relief

3. Melinda's grandmother, to whom she was very close, died of a long illness on Sunday afternoon. On Monday morning, Melinda's mother is astonished to find Melinda getting ready for school as she does every Monday morning. Which reaction is Melinda having?
   (A) Loneliness
   (B) Denial
   (C) Relief
   (D) Guilt
   (E) Regret

4. Micah's best friend, Lawrence, died of cancer at the age of 45. Whenever Micah spends time with the friends that they had in common, he is reminded of Lawrence and feels sad. He is not as close to his other friends as he was to Lawrence, and he feels he has no one to confide in with Lawrence gone. Which reaction is he having?
   (A) Shock
   (B) Denial
   (C) Anger
   (D) Loneliness
   (E) Guilt

5. Theresa's 9-year-old son went to a pool party for a friend's birthday and accidentally drowned. Theresa has been unable to forgive herself for letting him go to the party. What reaction is she having?
   (A) Anger
   (B) Loneliness
   (C) Denial
   (D) Guilt
   (E) Shock

6. Casey's brother was killed suddenly in a car accident. He is surprised that he seems to feel very little emotion regarding the death. Which reaction is Casey having?
   (A) Relief
   (B) Shock
   (C) Guilt
   (D) Anger
   (E) Regret

7. When Elizabeth's boyfriend was killed by a drunk driver on his way home one night, Elizabeth was inconsolable. She has stopped seeing her friends and stays in her room crying for hours at a time. Which reaction is she having?
   (A) Anger
   (B) Sadness
   (C) Guilt
   (D) Denial
   (E) Regret

8. Marcela's father recently died after battling congestive heart failure for many years. When he got sicker, Marcela had to take a leave of absence from work to help deal with his care, which greatly affected her income and caused her worry. She found herself resenting him at times. After he died, Marcela felt sad, but she also thinks about how she is free to make her own decisions about her life again. Which reaction is she having?
   (A) Anger
   (B) Denial
   (C) Relief
   (D) Guilt
   (E) Loneliness

3. Discuss how feelings and attitudes about death differ

Short Answer

1. Have you ever experienced the death of a loved one? If so, what are some of the emotions you felt?

_____

_____

_____

_____

_____

_____

_____

_____

2. What, if any, religious beliefs do you subscribe to? How do they influence your feelings about death? If you do not have any religious or spiritual beliefs, what are your feelings about death?

_____

_____

_____

_____

_____

_____

_____

3. What cultural background do you have? What cultures are you familiar with? Briefly describe how your culture or other cultures you are familiar with feel about death.

_____

_____

_____

_____

_____

_____

_____

_____

4. Discuss how to care for a client who is dying

True or False

1. _____ Advance directives do not need to be honored if the medical professional feels he can save the person's life.

2. _____ Listening to a client who is dying is very important.

3. _____ Hearing is usually the last sense to leave the body so the home health aide should continue to speak in a normal tone.

4. _____ When a person is dying, he no longer needs skin care.

5. _____ Keeping the room softly lit is best for a client who is dying.

6. _____ It is important for home health aides to observe clients for signs of pain as they may not be able to communicate that they are in pain.

7. _____ Back massage is one way to help clients who are in pain.

8. ____   It is best to keep a client who is dying isolated (by himself).

9. ____   To help a client who is dying to think positively, the home health aide can tell the client that he will most likely recover.

5. Explain legal rights for clients who are dying and describe ways to promote dignity

Short Answer

1. List three legal rights that must be honored when working with clients who are dying.

_____

_____

_____

2. Look at the *The Dying Person's Bill of Rights* on page 336 of your textbook. Pick three rights that you feel would be most important to you personally. Briefly describe why they would be important to you.

_____

_____

_____

_____

_____

_____

_____

_____

_____

_____

_____

_____

6. Define the goals of a hospice program and identify guidelines for hospice work

Multiple Choice

1. Hospice care is the term for compassionate care given to
   (A) Clients who have respiratory diseases
   (B) Clients who are dying
   (C) Clients with Parkinson's disease
   (D) Clients with developmental disabilities

2. Hospice care encourages clients to
   (A) Allow hospice care teams to handle all care decisions
   (B) Allow lawyers to make care decisions
   (C) Allow doctors to make care decisions
   (D) Participate in their own care as much as possible

3. Hospice goals focus on
   (A) Recovery of the person
   (B) Comfort and dignity of the person
   (C) Curing disease
   (D) Creating a will and other legal documents for the person

4. Focusing on pain relief, controlling symptoms, and preventing complications is called _____ care.
   (A) Palliative
   (B) Personal
   (C) Professional
   (D) Pediatric

Short Answer

5. List seven guidelines that are helpful for hospice work.

_____

_____

_____

_____

_____

_____

_____

_____

_____

_____

6. How do you alleviate stress in your life?

_____
_____
_____
_____
_____
_____
_____
_____

7. What are three ways you can take care of yourself?

_____
_____
_____
_____
_____
_____
_____
_____
_____
_____

7. Explain common signs of approaching death

Short Answer

Place a check mark (✓) beside the signs of approaching death.

1. ____ High blood pressure
2. ____ Fever
3. ____ Cold, pale skin
4. ____ Disorientation

5. ____ Healthy skin tone
6. ____ Heightened sense of touch
7. ____ Impaired speech
8. ____ Incontinence
9. ____ Perspiration
10. ____ Strong pulse

8. Describe postmortem care

Multiple Choice

1. After death, the muscles in the body become
    (A) Warm and pulsating
    (B) Bendable
    (C) Stiff and rigid
    (D) Hot and sharp

2. Caring for a body after death is called
    (A) Postmortem care
    (B) Mortician care
    (C) Funeral home care
    (D) Before-burial care

3. After death, the home health aide should place drainage pads under the body. These pads are most often needed
    (A) Under the arms
    (B) Under the perineum
    (C) Under the axillary area
    (D) Under the feet

4. If family members would like to remain with their loved one's body after death, the home health aide (HHA) should
    (A) Let them do so
    (B) Inform them that the HHA needs to ask the doctor first
    (C) Ask them to perform the postmortem care since they are staying with the body
    (D) Talk to them about the importance of organ donation

9. Understand and respect different postmortem practices

True or False

1. ____ Most people grieve in the same way.

2. _____ Some people like to remain with the body to perform religious rituals.

3. _____ The overall mood at a wake is usually very sad and somber.

4. _____ Having an open casket means the preserved body will be displayed to others.

5. _____ Some people will choose to be cremated, which means the body is burned until it is reduced to ashes.

6. _____ Readings of religious scripture and prayers may take place at a funeral.

7. _____ An atheist's funeral will normally involve prayers, hymns, and other religious rituals.

8. _____ The home health aide should remain professional and respectful whether or not he agrees with the rituals that take place after a client has died.

21

Clean, Safe, and Healthy Environments

1. Describe how housekeeping affects physical and psychological well-being

Short Answer

What are some reasons that home health aides should maintain an orderly and clean household for their clients?

_____

_____

_____

_____

_____

_____

_____

_____

_____

_____

2. List qualities needed to manage a home and describe general housekeeping guidelines

True or False

1. _____ The home health aide's (HHA) primary responsibility is to clean the client's kitchen.

2. _____ The HHA should expect that all members of the household will be able to help with housekeeping.

3. _____ One HHA assignment might be managing a client's finances.

4. _____ The HHA will need to be flexible with regard to household maintenance.

5. _____ Vacuuming is not part of an HHA's duties.

6. _____ Using proper body mechanics when performing housekeeping activities helps prevent injury.

7. _____ It is important for HHAs to be sensitive towards each client's customs and beliefs.

8. _____ The HHA will need to use cleaning materials and methods that are approved by clients and their families.

9. _____ The HHA should clean up and straighten up after every activity.

10. _____ One HHA responsibility is observing for infestation of insects and animals.

3. Describe cleaning products and equipment

True or False

1. _____ All-purpose cleaners can be used on several types of surfaces.

2. _____ For really dirty surfaces, it is best to use a mixture of bleach and ammonia.

3. _____ Abrasive cleaners are used mostly for bathing clients.

4. _____ A sponge is generally used to soften and remove soil on washable surfaces.

5. _____ Vacuum cleaner bags should be checked frequently.

6. _____ Some cleaning products can cause burns.

7. _____ Lemon juice is an example of an environmentally-friendly cleaning solution.

8. ____ White vinegar mixed with water can be used to clean glass.

9. ____ Baking soda is a type of toxic abrasive scouring powder.

4. Describe proper cleaning methods for living areas, kitchens, bathrooms, and storage areas

Multiple Choice

1. Examples of essential items that should be kept close by the client include
   (A) Eyeglasses
   (B) Potato chips
   (C) Nail polish
   (D) Cosmetics

2. Falls and accidents in the home are frequently caused by
   (A) Well-lit hallways
   (B) Wet floors
   (D) Clean floors
   (D) Leftover food scraps

3. In the kitchen, diseases may be transmitted by
   (A) Soap
   (B) Medications
   (C) Contaminated food surfaces
   (D) Bleach

4. It is a good idea for the home health aide to dust this frequently, unless the client has allergies
   (A) Five times a week
   (B) Once a week
   (C) Once every two months
   (D) Twice a month

5. If the freezer is not self-defrosting, the home health aide can quickly defrost it by
   (A) Using a warm knife to chip at the ice
   (B) Lighting matches near the ice
   (C) Holding a lighter near the ice
   (D) Placing pans of hot water in it

6. In order to remove odors, the home health aide can use
   (A) Flour
   (B) Baking soda
   (C) Sugar
   (D) Baking powder

7. Dishes can be sterilized by
   (A) Using a dishwasher
   (B) Using cold water
   (C) Using an oven cleaner
   (D) Drying them with a dish towel

8. How often should the home health aide dispose of garbage?
   (A) Daily
   (B) Weekly
   (C) Monthly
   (D) Every two weeks

9. Basic bathroom hygiene includes
   (A) Washing from dirty areas to clean areas
   (B) Placing soiled towels on the bathroom sink
   (C) Cleaning the tub and shower after each use
   (D) Leaving toothbrushes in the sink

10. Instead of glass cleaner, the home health aide can mix water and ____ to clean glass.
    (A) White wine
    (B) White vinegar
    (C) Apple juice
    (D) Spray starch

11. In what situation do mold and mildew grow best?
    (A) In extreme cold
    (B) In dry heat
    (C) In warm, moist places
    (D) In windy areas

12. Floors and rugs should be vacuumed at least
    (A) Once a month
    (B) Twice a week
    (C) Once a week
    (D) Once a day

13. Which of the following materials is commonly recycled?
    (A) Wood
    (B) Plastic
    (C) Polyester
    (D) Marble

5. Describe how to prepare a cleaning schedule

Short Answer

Create a sample cleaning schedule for an immobile client.

Immediately:

_____

_____

_____

_____

_____

Daily:

_____

_____

_____

_____

_____

Weekly:

_____

_____

_____

_____

_____

Monthly:

_____

_____

_____

_____

_____

Less often:

_____

_____

_____

_____

_____

6. List special housekeeping procedures to use when infection is present

Fill in the Blank

1. _____ any surfaces that come into contact with body fluids, such as

   _____,

   urinals, and toilets.

2. Frequently remove _____ containing used tissues.

3. Keep any _____ of urine, stool, or sputum in double bags away from food.

4. Take special _____ in housecleaning when the client has an infectious disease.

5. _____ dishes and utensils should be used for the client.

6. Wash dishes in hot, soapy water with _____, and rinse in _____ water.

7. _____ the client's bathroom daily.

7. Explain how to do laundry and care for clothes

Crossword

Across

2. What bleach must always be diluted with

5. Washing cycle used for delicate or fragile items

6. Washing cycle used for sturdy permanent press items and cottons

8. Type of bleach used on washable fabrics; most effective in hot water

Name: _____

9. Delicate fabric requires
_____ time in the dryer.

10. If clients can do their own mending, the HHA may just need to
_____ the needle.

11. Water temperature used for brightly-colored fabrics

13. One way to reduce these is to fold clothes immediately after they are dried

Down

1. Water temperature used for whites and towels

2. Liquid chlorine bleach does this to clothing in addition to removing stains

3. The safest water temperature for most garments

4. If dirty or stained laundry items were specially treated before washing, they were
_____.

7. Must be cleaned every time the dryer is used

11. Parts of a shirt that should be ironed first, after collars

12. Pressing dark fabrics and silks on the wrong side helps prevent them from looking like this

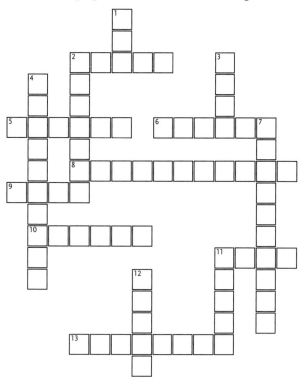

8. List special laundry precautions to use when infection is present

True or False

1. _____ It is best to use cold water when doing laundry for a client who has an infectious disease.

2. _____ The home health aide should wear gloves when doing the laundry for a client who has an infectious disease.

3. _____ Dirty laundry should be shaken to remove dirt before putting it in the washing machine.

4. _____ The home health aide should keep the client's laundry separate from other family members' laundry.

5. _____ Dirty laundry should remain in the client's room as long as possible so as to avoid contamination of the rest of the house.

6. _____ Agency-approved disinfectants should be used in loads of laundry.

9. List guidelines for teaching housekeeping skills to clients' family members

Scenario
Read the following scenario and decide how to respond.

Dave, a home health aide, is explaining to Mrs. Crawford's family how to protect against infectious diseases when doing the laundry and cleaning the kitchen. He has written a long list of instructions, and when he is done explaining, two family members still seem confused about some key points. How should Dave respond in this situation?

_____
_____
_____
_____
_____
_____

_____
_____
_____
_____
_____
_____
_____
_____
_____

10. Discuss the importance of sleep and explain why careful bedmaking is important

Multiple Choice

1. Why is it important for home health aides (HHAs) to change bed linens often?
   (A) To get clients out of their beds and moving around
   (B) To rotate clean sheets evenly
   (C) To keep skills up-to-date
   (D) To prevent infection and to promote comfort

2. When removing dirty linen, the HHA should
   (A) Fold it so that the soiled area is outside
   (B) Roll it so that the soiled area is inside
   (C) Gather it in a bunch
   (D) Shake it to remove particles

3. A bed made with the bedspread and blankets in place is called a(n)
   (A) Open bed
   (B) Stretcher bed
   (C) Closed bed
   (D) Completed bed

11. Identify hazardous household materials

Short Answer

Identify five hazardous household materials.

_____
_____
_____
_____
_____

Name: _____

22

Clients' Nutritional Needs

1. Describe the importance of proper nutrition and list the six basic nutrients

Short Answer
Write the letter of the correct basic nutrient beside each description below. Use a W for water, C for carbohydrates, P for protein, F for fats, V for vitamins, and M for minerals. Letters may be used more than once.

1. _____ Sources include seafood, dried beans, poultry, and soy products.

2. _____ A person can survive only a few days without this.

3. _____ These build bones and help in blood formation.

4. _____ These add flavor to food and help to absorb certain vitamins.

5. _____ Examples include bread, cereal, and potatoes.

6. _____ They are essential for tissue growth and repair.

7. _____ The body cannot make most of these nutrients; they must be obtained through certain foods.

8. _____ They provide fiber, which is necessary for bowel elimination.

9. _____ May come from olives, nuts, and dairy products

10. _____ Most essential nutrient for life

11. _____ Categories include monounsaturated and saturated.

12. _____ Helps to maintain body temperature through perspiration

13. _____ Can be fat-soluble or water-soluble

14. _____ These help the body store energy.

15. _____ Iron and calcium are examples.

2. Describe the USDA's MyPlate

Short Answer
The USDA developed the MyPlate icon and website to help promote healthy eating practices. Looking at the MyPlate icon, fill in the food groups.

1. _____

2. _____

3. _____

4. _____

5. _____

Short Answer
Read the following descriptions and mark which each is describing—V for vegetables, F for fruits, G for grains, P for protein, and D for dairy. Letters will be used more than once.

6. _____ This group includes foods that retain their calcium content, such as yogurt and cheese.

Name: _____

7. _____ This includes all foods made from wheat, rice, oats, cornmeal, and barley.

8. _____ Plant sources of this include beans and soy products.

9. _____ Eating seafood twice a week in place of meat or poultry is recommended for this group.

10. _____ Most choices from this group should be fat-free or low-fat.

11. _____ Important sources of dietary fiber and many nutrients, including folic acid and vitamin C.

12. _____ Half of a person's plate should consist of choices from these two groups.

13. _____ At least half of all of these consumed should be "whole."

14. _____ One subgroup of these contains the bran, germ, and endosperm.

15. _____ These products contain calcium, potassium, vitamin D, and protein.

16. _____ Within this group, dark green, red, and orange types have the best nutritional content.

17. _____ Animal sources of this include meat, poultry, seafood, and eggs.

Multiple Choice

18. MyPlate's guidelines state that half of a person's plate should be made up of
   (A) Grains and protein
   (B) Vegetables and fruits
   (C) Seafood and dairy
   (D) Grains and dairy

19. Vegetables that are this color have the best nutritional content:
   (A) Dark green
   (B) Light yellow
   (C) Purple
   (D) Brown

20. Most of a person's fruit choices should be
   (A) Frozen fruit
   (B) Smoothies
   (C) Cut-up fruit
   (D) Fruit juice

21. What kinds of grains are best to consume?
   (A) Refined grains
   (B) White grains
   (C) Whole grains
   (D) Corn grains

22. Which of the following is considered a plant-based protein?
   (A) Salmon
   (B) Eggs
   (C) Sausage
   (D) Beans

23. Oatmeal and pasta are examples of foods made from which food group?
   (A) Vegetables
   (B) Fruits
   (C) Grains
   (D) Protein

24. Most dairy group choices should be
   (A) Whole-fat
   (B) 2% fat
   (C) 1/2 and 1/2
   (D) 1% fat

25. Which of the following foods is considered high in sodium?
   (A) Apple
   (B) Pickle
   (C) Avocado
   (D) Corn

3. Identify ways to assist clients in maintaining fluid balance

True or False

1. _____ Twenty-four ounces of water per day is the recommended amount for most people.

2. _____ Fluid overload occurs when the body is unable to handle the amount of fluid consumed.

3. _____ The sense of thirst diminishes in elderly people.

4. _____ People can become dehydrated by vomiting too much.

5. _____ If a client has an NPO order, he can drink water but no other type of fluid.

Name: _____

6. ____ In order to prevent dehydration, the home health aide should encourage clients who do not have fluid restrictions to drink every time she sees them.

7. ____ One symptom of dehydration is dark urine.

4. Identify nutritional problems of the elderly or ill

Crossword
Across

4. Type of tube placed into the stomach through the abdominal wall for feeding a person (abbreviation)

5. Type of liquid that may be used for someone who has difficulty swallowing

Down

1. Skin breakdown due to weight loss can lead to these problems

2. Position clients should be in for eating

3. Temperature of food that may be preferable for someone suffering from nausea

Short Answer
Make a check mark (✓) by all of the correct guidelines for working with clients who require tube feedings.

6. ____ The home health aide (HHA) should remove the tube when the feeding is finished.

7. ____ During the feeding, the client should remain in a sitting position with the head of the bed elevated at least 45 degrees.

8. ____ Redness or drainage around the opening should be reported.

9. ____ HHAs are responsible for slowly pouring feedings into the tube.

10. ____ HHAs should give careful skin care for clients who must remain in bed for long periods to help prevent pressure injuries.

11. ____ It is important for the HHA to wash his hands before assisting in any way with a tube feeding.

12. ____ After a client has had a tube feeding, the HHA should help the client to lie down flat on his back.

5. Demonstrate awareness of regional, cultural, and religious food preferences

Short Answer

Briefly describe some of the foods you ate while growing up. Were there any special dishes that your family made that were related to your culture, religion, or region?

_____
_____
_____
_____
_____
_____
_____

Name: _____

_____
_____
_____
_____

6. List and define common health claims on food labels

Fill in the Blank

1. _____ meat, poultry, eggs, and dairy products come from animals that are given no antibiotics or growth hormones.

2. _____ products may contain artificial sweeteners, such as saccharin or aspartame.

3. If a product is labeled
   _____ or
   _____, it usually does not contain much fat.

4. The claims of
   _____,
   healthy, or *good for you* may have little or no meaning.

5. Clients who must reduce their sodium or salt intake should eat foods labeled
   _____,
   _____, or
   _____.

6. The best way to limit
   _____ is to avoid foods containing animal fats.

7. If a product is labeled
   _____, it means that the chickens producing the eggs have been allowed access to the outside for an unspecified period of time.

7. Explain the information on the FDA-required Nutrition Facts label

Multiple Choice

1. If more than ___% of total daily calories comes from added sugars, it may be difficult to stay within calorie limits.
   (A) 30%
   (B) 50%
   (C) 10%
   (D) 2%

2. Which of the following minerals is required to be on the nutrition facts label?
   (A) Zinc
   (B) Selenium
   (C) Phosphate
   (D) Iron

3. The standardized nutrition label on all packaged foods is called
   (A) Percentage label
   (B) Food Information label
   (C) Nutrition Facts label
   (D) Serving Size Information label

4. The recommended daily totals on the label are based on a _____ calorie diet.
   (A) 2,500
   (B) 2,000
   (C) 1,000
   (D) 5,000

8. Explain special diets

Matching
For each of the following diets, choose the best description from those listed below. Use each letter only once.

1. _____ Bland Diet

2. _____ Diabetic Diet

3. _____ Fluid-Restricted Diet

4. _____ Gluten-Free Diet

5. _____ High-Potassium Diet

6. _____ High-Residue Diet

7. _____ Liquid Diet

8. _____ Low-Fat/Low-Cholesterol Diet

9. _____ Low-Protein Diet

10. ____ Low-Residue Diet

11. ____ Low-Sodium Diet

12. ____ Mechanical Soft Diet

13. ____ Modified Calorie Diet

14. ____ Pureed Diet

15. ____ Soft Diet

16. ____ Vegetarian Diet

(A) To prevent further heart or kidney damage, doctors may restrict fluid intake on this diet.

(B) This diet consists of foods that are in a liquid state at body temperature and is usually ordered as *clear* or *full*.

(C) This diet consists of soft or chopped foods that are easy to chew; foods that are hard to chew and swallow, such as raw vegetables, will be restricted.

(D) People who have kidney disease may also be on this diet, which encourages foods like breads and pasta.

(E) People at risk for heart attacks and heart disease may be placed on this diet. This diet permits skim milk, low-fat cottage cheese, fish, and white meat of turkey and chicken.

(F) Carb counting may be part of this diet, as the amount of carbohydrates eaten must be carefully regulated.

(G) Salt is restricted in this diet.

(H) This diet is used for losing weight or preventing weight gain.

(I) The food used in this diet has been ground into a thick paste of baby-food consistency.

(J) Often used for people who have gastric ulcers, this diet involves avoiding alcohol, spicy foods, and citrus juices, among other items.

(K) Health reasons, a dislike of meat, a compassion for animals, or a belief in non-violence may lead a person to this diet.

(L) Used for people with celiac disease, this diet eliminates foods containing wheat flour, such as tortillas, crackers, breads, and pasta.

(M) Foods high in this mineral will be encouraged in this diet; this includes bananas, prunes, dried apricots, figs, and sweet potatoes.

(N) This diet increases the amount of fiber and whole grains ingested; it helps prevent constipation.

(O) This diet is used for people who have bowel disorders and reduces the amount of fiber and whole grains ingested.

(P) Foods in this diet are chopped or blended and are prepared using blenders, food processors, meat grinders, or cutting utensils.

9. Describe guidelines for assisting with eating

Multiple Choice

1. In which position should clients be when they are eating?
   (A) Sitting upright
   (B) Reclining
   (C) Lying on their sides
   (D) Standing

2. Ways to promote a client's dignity while feeding include
   (A) Asking the client, "Can you eat quickly tonight? I've still got to give you a bath."
   (B) Asking the client, "Which food would you like to try first?"
   (C) Looking around the room while he is eating
   (D) Mixing food whether or not the client has requested it

3. What is the best way for the home health aide (HHA) to test the temperature of her client's food?
   (A) The HHA should touch the food before serving it.
   (B) The HHA should put the food in the freezer until the steam is gone.
   (C) The HHA should try a bite before the client does.
   (D) The HHA should put her hand over the dish to sense its heat.

True or False

4. ____ Clients who must be fed are often embarrassed and depressed about their dependence on another person.

5. ____ It is a good idea for the HHA to alternate offering food and drink while feeding.

6. ____ The HHA should stand while feeding a client.

7. ____ The HHA should give the client her full attention while the client is eating.

8. ____ The client's mouth should be empty before the HHA offers another bite of food.

9. ____ The HHA should refer to pureed green beans as "green stuff" so the client knows which dish the HHA is talking about.

10. Describe eating and swallowing problems a client may have

Multiple Choice

1. In order to prevent aspiration, the HHA should keep the client in the _____ position after eating for at least 30 minutes.
   (A) Upright
   (B) Reclining
   (C) Lying flat
   (D) Side

2. Which consistency refers to being the thickness of a thick juice, which is able to be drunk from a cup?
   (A) Honey
   (B) Pudding
   (C) Pear
   (D) Nectar

3. The medical term for difficulty in swallowing is
   (A) Aspiration
   (B) Dysphagia
   (C) Edema
   (D) Diuretic

4. If a client has a doctor's order for thickened liquids, which of the following can the HHA offer to the client?
   (A) Water
   (B) Thickened soup
   (C) Broth
   (D) Milk

5. Which consistency refers to the liquid being semi-solid, in which a spoon can stand up straight in the glass?
   (A) Honey
   (B) Pudding
   (C) Pear
   (D) Nectar

23

Meal Planning, Shopping, Preparation, and Storage

1. Explain how to prepare a basic food plan and list food shopping guidelines

Short Answer
Make a basic food plan for Monday through Friday. Include breakfast, lunch, dinner, and snacks.

MONDAY

Breakfast

Snack

Lunch

Snack

Dinner

Snack

TUESDAY

Breakfast

Snack

Lunch

Snack

Dinner

Snack

WEDNESDAY

Breakfast

Snack

Lunch

Snack

Dinner

Snack

THURSDAY

Breakfast

Snack

Lunch

Snack

Dinner

Snack

Name: _____

FRIDAY
_____

Breakfast

Snack

Lunch

Snack

Dinner

Snack
_____

Fill in the Blank

1. Avoid _____,
   already-mixed, or ready-made foods because
   they are more expensive.

2. Read _____ for
   ingredients that may be harmful to a client,
   such as excessive salt.

3. Estimate the _____
   by dividing the total cost by the number of
   servings.

4. For clients on a low-fat diet, take the
   _____ off chicken
   and turkey parts.

5. Buy fresh foods that are in season when they
   are at their _____
   flavor.

6. Large amounts or larger sizes are usually
   more _____.

7. Cheaper cuts of meat tend to have more
   _____ in bones
   and fat.

Short Answer

8. List four factors to consider when buying
   food for clients.

   _____

   _____

_____
_____
_____

9. Do you buy any organic and/or locally-grown
   foods? If so, why is that important to you?

   _____

   _____

   _____

   _____

   _____

2. List guidelines for safe food preparation

True or False

1. ____ The home health aide (HHA) should
   wash his hands before handling food,
   but does not need to wash his hands
   again afterward.

2. ____ Sponges should be washed in the
   dishwasher to disinfect them.

3. ____ It is a good idea to defrost frozen
   foods on the counter.

4. ____ Food can be left out safely for five
   hours.

5. ____ Poultry needs to be cooked thoroughly
   to kill microorganisms.

6. ____ If the HHA sneezes while around
   food, she should wash her hands
   again.

7. ____ It is best to use separate cutting
   boards for meat and vegetables.

8. ____ It is not necessary to change knives
   between cutting fresh meat and
   vegetables.

9. ____ If a person has a weakened immune
   system because of cancer, a foodborne
   illness can be deadly.

10. ____ Elderly people are at increased risk for
    foodborne illnesses because they do
    not care about how food tastes.

3. Identify methods of food preparation

Matching
For each method of food preparation, identify the correct description. Use each letter only once.

1. ____ Baking

2. ____ Boiling

3. ____ Braising

4. ____ Broiling

5. ____ Frying

6. ____ Microwaving

7. ____ Poaching

8. ____ Roasting

9. ____ Sautéing

10. ____ Steaming

(A) Safe for defrosting, reheating, and cooking, but this method can cause cold spots.

(B) Cooked in barely boiling water or other liquids; this is an ideal way to prepare fish and eggs.

(C) Used for meats, poultry, and some vegetables, this method may involve mixing items with oils or spices before cooking and basting meats or poultry during cooking.

(D) The best method for cooking pasta, noodles, and rice.

(E) Used in an oven at a moderate heat, this method is appropriate for many foods such as breads, fish, vegetables, and casseroles.

(F) A quick way to cook vegetables and meats by using a small amount of oil in a frying pan and stirring constantly.

(G) A small amount of water is boiled in the bottom of a saucepan, and food is set over it in a basket or colander.

(H) The least healthy way to cook, this method uses a lot of fat.

(I) This method can be used to melt cheese or brown the top of a casserole.

(J) A slow-cooking method that uses moist heat to cook meat or vegetables at a temperature just below boiling.

4. Identify four methods of low-fat food preparation

Fill in the Blank

1. _____ allows fats in meat to drip out before food is consumed, which lowers fat content.

2. Plan meals around _____ to help cut out the fat content.

3. Sometimes high-fat ingredients can be _____ or replaced to lower the fat content of a recipe.

4. _____ meat on paper towels after you brown it.

5. Leave out _____ on sandwiches or on top of casseroles.

6. An example of a low-fat meal based on grains is beans and _____.

7. Boiling, steaming, broiling, roasting, and _____ are all methods of cooking that require little fat.

8. Try substituting _____ for mayonnaise or sour cream.

5. List four guidelines for safe food storage

Multiple Choice

1. After shopping, which of the following foods should be put away first?
   (A) Crackers
   (B) Milk
   (C) Pasta
   (D) Cereal

2. It is a good idea to keep easily-spoiled items in the
   (A) Door of the refrigerator
   (B) Cupboard
   (C) Rear of the refrigerator
   (D) Pantry

3. Refrigerator temperature should be between
    (A) 0°F - 10°F
    (B) 36°F - 40°F
    (C) 10°F - 20°F
    (D) 62°F - 66°F

4. Food should not be left out for more than
    _____ hours.
    (A) Five
    (B) Three
    (C) Two
    (D) Twelve

5. If the home health aide is not sure whether
    food is spoiled, she should
    (A) Discard it
    (B) Serve it and see if anyone complains or
        feels ill
    (C) Cook it for a longer time than usual
    (D) Smell it after cooking it to be sure it is
        safe

6. Foods that can be composted include
    (A) Canola oil
    (B) Fish bones
    (C) Yogurt
    (D) Coffee grounds

24

Managing Time, Energy, and Money

1. Explain three ways to work more efficiently

Short Answer

1. For each of the three ways of working more efficiently described in this learning objective, give an example (other than what is in the book) of how you can put the method into action.

_____

_____

_____

_____

_____

_____

_____

_____

_____

_____

_____

_____

_____

_____

2. List five ways to conserve time and energy.

_____

_____

_____

_____

_____

_____

2. Describe how to follow an established work plan with the client and family

Short Answer

Pick the busiest day you will have next week, and draft a work plan for that day. List tasks to complete and prioritize them.

_____

_____

_____

_____

_____

_____

_____

_____

_____

_____

_____

_____

_____

_____

3. Discuss ways to handle inappropriate requests

Scenario

Read the following scenario and answer the question.

Richard, a home health aide, is preparing to leave his client's home for the day. Mr. Perez, his client, demands that Richard buy him some soup at the grocery store before he leaves. This errand is not in the care plan, but Mr. Perez tells him that he really wants some soup. Mr. Perez begins to cry. What should Richard do in this situation?

_____

_____

_____

_____

_____

_____

_____

_____

_____

4. List five money-saving homemaking tips

Short Answer

List and briefly explain the five money-saving tips.

_____

_____

_____

_____

_____

_____

_____

_____

_____

_____

5. List guidelines for handling a client's money

Short Answer

1. What are your state's guidelines for handling a client's money?

_____

_____

_____

_____

_____

_____

True or False

2. _____ It is fine for a home health aide (HHA) to use her client's money for her own things as long as she pays it back soon.

3. _____ It is a good idea for the HHA to estimate the amount of money he will need before requesting it.

4. _____ The HHA should return receipts to the client or family member as soon as possible.

5. _____ The HHA should keep a client's cash separate from her own.

6. _____ If a client is unsure about his budget, the HHA should give him financial advice and budgeting tips.

25

Caring for Yourself and Your Career

1. Discuss different types of careers in the healthcare field

True or False

1. _____ Direct service workers include salespeople, waiters, and bartenders.

2. _____ X-ray technicians work in diagnostic services.

3. _____ Receptionists, office managers, and billing staff are considered part of the healthcare field.

4. _____ Health educators have job opportunities within the healthcare field.

5. _____ Counselors and social workers are not part of the healthcare field.

2. Explain how to find a job

Short Answer

List three resources you should try when looking for potential employers.

_____

_____

_____

_____

_____

_____

_____

3. Identify documents that may be required when applying for a job and explain how to write a résumé

Short Answer

1. List four documents that may be needed when applying for a job.

_____

_____

_____

_____

_____

True or False

2. _____ Friends and relatives are the best references to use for a potential job.

3. _____ A person's résumé should fit on one page.

4. _____ A résumé should include a list of the person's educational experience.

5. _____ A résumé should include a list of the person's religious and political beliefs.

6. _____ If a potential employer asks a person for proof of his legal status in this country, it means that the employer is being discriminatory.

7. _____ A cover letter should emphasize the skills that would be a good match for the position a person is seeking.

4. Demonstrate completing an effective job application

Short Answer
Complete the sample job application.

Employment Application

Personal Information

Name:	Date:

Home Address:

City, State, Zip:

Email Address:

Home Phone:	Business Phone:
US Citizen?	If Not, Give Visa No. and Expiration Date:

Position Applying For

Title	Salary Desired:
Referred By:	Date Available:

Education

High School (Name, City, State):

Graduation Date:

Technical or Undergraduate School:

Dates Attended:	Degree Major:

References

5. Demonstrate competence in job interview techniques

Short Answer
Make a check mark (✓) next to the actions appropriate for job interviews.

1. ____ Wearing jeans

2. ____ Looking happy to be there

3. ____ Asking if it is okay to smoke during the interview

4. ____ Wearing very little jewelry

5. ____ Asking how many hours you would work

6. ____ Bringing your child with you when you cannot find a babysitter

7. ____ Wearing your nicest perfume

8. ____ Sitting up straight

9. ____ Asking what benefits the employer offers

10. ____ Shaking hands with interviewer

11. ____ Eating a granola bar during the interview

12. ____ Asking if you got the job at the end of the interview

6. Discuss appropriate responses to feedback

Short Answer
Read the following and mark whether they are examples of constructive feedback or hostile criticism. Use a C for constructive and an H for hostile.

1. ____ "You are a horrible person."

2. ____ "If you weren't so slow, things might get done around here."

3. ____ "Some of your reports are not complete; try to be more accurate."

4. ____ "That was the worst meal I've ever eaten!"

5. ____ "I'm not sure that you understood what I meant. Let me rephrase the issue."

6. ____ "Where did you learn how to clean?"

7. ____ "That was a stupid idea."

8. ____ "That procedure could have been performed in a more efficient way."

9. ____ "Try to make more of an effort to listen carefully."

10. ____ "Stop being so lazy."

7. Identify effective ways to make a complaint to an employer or supervisor and discuss how to manage conflict

Scenario
Read the following scenario and answer the question.

Anne is a home health aide who works three days a week for her client, Mrs. Singer. Generally, Mrs. Singer's son, Benjamin, is there as well, and Anne and he work as a team. Benjamin finds a new job and cannot be home during the day anymore. The next time Anne arrives, Mrs. Singer is moody and distant. She is reluctant to follow the care plan, and she tells Anne that she will not take a bath until Benjamin comes home. She also refuses to eat food that Anne has cooked, insisting she can only eat her son's cooking. After some gentle urging, Anne gets Mrs. Singer to eat and take a bath.

The next time Anne works, Mrs. Singer drops her plate on the floor and tells Anne that she is a lousy cook. She tells her to fix a new meal and clean up the mess. Anne does both, although she feels very upset.

Should this be reported to a supervisor? If so, how?

_____

_____

_____

_____

_____

_____

_____

_____

_____

_____

_____

_____

Multiple Choice

2. When is an appropriate time to discuss an issue that is causing conflict in the workplace?
   (A) When the home health aide (HHA) decides she cannot take it anymore
   (B) When the HHA is upset because something has just occurred
   (C) Right before the HHA gives her notice
   (D) When the supervisor has decided on a proper time and place

3. When trying to resolve a conflict, the HHA should
   (A) Interrupt the other person if the HHA might forget what she is going to say
   (B) Sit back in the chair with her arms crossed over her chest
   (C) Take turns speaking
   (D) Yell at the other person if it seems like her point is not understood

4. When discussing conflict, the HHA should
   (A) State how she feels when a behavior occurs
   (B) Name-call
   (C) Not look the other person in the eye
   (D) Keep the TV on to fill awkward silences

5. To resolve a conflict, the HHA should be prepared to
   (A) Compromise
   (B) Quit
   (C) Yell
   (D) Interrupt

8. Identify guidelines for making job changes

Fill in the Blank

1. The home health aide (HHA) should always give an employer _____ weeks' written notice that he will be leaving.

2. Potential future employers may talk with the HHA's past _____.

3. If an HHA decides to change jobs, he should be _____.

9. List your state's requirements for maintaining certification

Short Answer

1. How many hours of in-service education are required each year by your state?

_____

_____

2. How long is an absence from working allowed, without retraining, in your state?

_____

_____

_____

10. Describe continuing education for home health aides

True or False

1. _____ The federal government requires 20 hours of continuing education each year.

2. _____ Treatments or regulations can change.

3. _____ States require less continuing education than the federal government.

4. _____ In-service continuing education courses help keep knowledge fresh.

Short Answer

5. List three of the responsibilities a home health aide has regarding continuing education.

_____

_____

_____

_____

_____

_____

_____

_____

_____

11. Define stress and stressors and list examples

Short Answer

What are some things that make you experience stress? How do you react when you are stressed?

_____

_____

_____

_____

_____

_____

_____

_____

_____

_____

_____

12. Explain ways to manage stress

Multiple Choice

1. Stress is a _____ response.
   - (A) Relaxation
   - (B) Physical and emotional
   - (C) Rare
   - (D) Supervisory

2. When the heart beats fast in stressful situations, it can be a result of the increase of the hormone
   - (A) Testosterone
   - (B) Estrogen
   - (C) Adrenaline
   - (D) Progesterone

3. A healthy lifestyle includes
   - (A) Eating when a person is not hungry to calm down
   - (B) Exercising regularly
   - (C) Smoking a few cigarettes a week
   - (D) Complaining about a job

4. Which of the following is a sign that a person is not managing stress?
   - (A) Preparing meals ahead of time
   - (B) Taking deep breaths and relaxing
   - (C) Feeling alert and positive
   - (D) Not being able to focus on work

5. Which of the following are appropriate people for a home health aide to turn to for help in managing stress?
   - (A) Clients
   - (B) Supervisors
   - (C) Clients' family members
   - (D) Clients' friends

13. Demonstrate two effective relaxation techniques

Short Answer

Try one of the relaxation techniques listed on page 407 of the textbook. Describe how you felt after the experience.

_____

_____

_____

14. Describe how to develop a personal stress management plan

Short Answer

Write out your own personal stress management plan. Be sure to include things like diet, exercise, relaxation exercises, entertainment, etc.

Name: _____

15. List five guidelines for managing time

Short Answer

List five guidelines for managing time.

_____

_____

_____

_____

_____

_____

16. Demonstrate an understanding of the basics of money management

Short Answer

List five guidelines for managing money.

_____

_____

_____

_____

_____

_____

_____

17. Demonstrate an understanding that money matters are emotional

Short Answer

When was the last time you wanted something you could not afford? How did it make you feel? What did you do?

_____

_____

_____

_____

_____

_____

_____

_____

_____

_____

_____

_____

_____

_____

18. List ways to remind yourself that your work is important, valuable, and meaningful

Short Answer

1. List five things that you have learned in this course that have surprised or excited you.

_____

_____

_____

_____

_____

_____

_____

_____

_____

_____

_____

_____

_____

_____

Name: _____

2. List five things that you are looking forward
    to doing when you start working as a home
    health aide.

    _____

    _____

    _____

    _____

    _____

    _____

    _____

    _____

    _____

    _____

    _____

    _____

    _____

    _____

    _____

Name: _____

Name: _____

Procedure Checklists

5
Infection Prevention and Standard Precautions

Washing hands (hand hygiene)

		yes	no
1.	Turns on water at sink.		
2.	Wets hands and wrists thoroughly.		
3.	Applies soap to hands.		
4.	Keeps hands lower than elbows and fingertips down. Rubs hands together and lathers all surfaces of wrists, fingers, and hands, using friction for at least 20 seconds.		
5.	Cleans nails by rubbing them in palm of other hand.		
6.	Keeps hands lower than elbows and fingertips down. Without touching sink, rinses all surfaces of hands and wrists, running water from wrists to fingertips.		
7.	Uses clean, dry paper towel to dry all surfaces of hands, wrists, and fingers. Disposes of towel without touching container.		
8.	Uses clean, dry paper towel to turn off faucet and disposes of used paper towel, without contaminating hands.		

_____   _____
Date Reviewed   Instructor Signature

_____   _____
Date Performed   Instructor Signature

Putting on (donning) and removing (doffing) gown

		yes	no
1.	Washes hands.		
2.	Opens gown and allows it to unfold without shaking it. Places arms through each sleeve.		
3.	Fastens neck opening and pulls gown until it completely covers clothing. Secures gown at waist.		
4.	Puts on gloves after putting on gown.		
5.	When removing gown, removes and discards gloves first. Then unfastens gown at neck and waist.		
6.	Removes gown without touching the outside of gown. Rolls dirty side in while holding gown away from body. Disposes of gown. Washes hands.		

_____   _____
Date Reviewed   Instructor Signature

_____   _____
Date Performed   Instructor Signature

Putting on (donning) mask and goggles

		yes	no
1.	Washes hands.		
2.	Picks up mask by top strings or elastic strap. Does not touch mask where it touches face.		
3.	Pulls elastic strap over head or ties top strings first, then bottom strings if mask has strings.		
4.	Pinches the metal strip at the top of the mask tightly around nose. Fits mask snugly around face and below chin.		
5.	Puts on goggles.		
6.	Puts on gloves.		

_____   _____
Date Reviewed   Instructor Signature

_____   _____
Date Performed   Instructor Signature

Name: _____

Putting on (donning) gloves

		yes	no
1.	Washes hands.		
2.	If right-handed, slides one glove on left hand (reverses if left-handed).		
3.	With gloved hand, slides other hand into the second glove.		
4.	Interlaces fingers to smooth out folds and create a comfortable fit.		
5.	Carefully looks for tears, holes, cracks, or spots. Replaces glove if needed.		
6.	Adjusts gloves for correct fit. If wearing a gown, pulls the cuff of the gloves over sleeves of gown.		

_____   _____
Date Reviewed   Instructor Signature

_____   _____
Date Performed   Instructor Signature

Removing (doffing) gloves

		yes	no
1.	Touches only the outside of one glove and grasps the other glove at the palm, pulling glove off.		
2.	With ungloved hand, slips two fingers underneath cuff of remaining glove. Does not touch any part of the outside of glove.		
3.	Pulls down, turning glove inside out and over the first glove. One glove from its clean inner side should be holding the other glove inside it.		
4.	Discards gloves.		
5.	Washes hands.		

_____   _____
Date Reviewed   Instructor Signature

_____   _____
Date Performed   Instructor Signature

Disinfecting using wet heat

		yes	no
1.	Washes hands.		
2.	Places items in the pot and fills it with water, covering all items.		
3.	Places lid on pot and places pot on stove.		
4.	Turns on heat and brings water to a boil. Boils for 20 minutes.		
5.	Turns off heat. Allows items and water to cool.		
6.	After items have cooled, removes cover and then items. Places items on rack to dry.		
7.	Washes and dries equipment. Returns to proper storage.		
8.	Washes hands.		
9.	Documents procedure.		

_____   _____
Date Reviewed   Instructor Signature

_____   _____
Date Performed   Instructor Signature

Disinfecting using dry heat

		yes	no
1.	Washes hands.		
2.	Places items in the pan and places pan or sheet in oven.		
3.	Turns on oven to 350° F and bakes for one hour.		
4.	Turns off heat. Allows items to cool.		
5.	After items have cooled, removes items.		
6.	Stores items.		
7.	Washes and dries equipment. Returns to proper storage.		
8.	Washes hands.		
9.	Documents procedure.		

_____   _____
Date Reviewed   Instructor Signature

_____   _____
Date Performed   Instructor Signature

Name: ______________________________

7
Emergency Care and Disaster Preparation

Performing abdominal thrusts for the conscious person			
		yes	no
1.	Stands behind person and brings arms under person's arms. Wraps arms around person's waist.		
2.	Makes a fist with one hand. Places flat, thumb side of the fist against person's abdomen, above the navel but below the breastbone.		
3.	Grasps the fist with other hand. Pulls both hands toward self and up, quickly and forcefully.		
4.	Repeats until object is pushed out or person loses consciousness.		
5.	Reports and documents incident.		

Date Reviewed ____________ Instructor Signature ____________

Date Performed ____________ Instructor Signature ____________

Clearing an obstructed airway in a conscious infant			
		yes	no
1.	Lays the infant face down on forearm; if sitting, rests the arm holding the infant's torso on lap or thigh. Supports infant's jaw and head with hand.		
2.	Delivers up to five back blows.		
3.	If the obstruction is not expelled, turns infant onto his back while supporting the head. Delivers up to five chest thrusts.		
4.	Repeats, alternating five back blows and five chest thrusts until object is pushed out or infant loses consciousness.		
5.	Reports and documents incident.		

Date Reviewed ____________ Instructor Signature ____________

Date Performed ____________ Instructor Signature ____________

Responding to shock			
		yes	no
1.	Calls for help immediately.		
2.	Puts on gloves and controls bleeding if necessary.		
3.	Has the person lie down on her back unless bleeding from the mouth or vomiting. Elevates the legs unless person has a head, neck, back, spinal, or abdominal injury; breathing difficulties; or fractures.		
4.	Checks pulse and respirations if possible. Begins CPR if breathing and pulse are absent.		
5.	Keeps person as calm and comfortable as possible.		
6.	Maintains normal body temperature.		
7.	Does not give person anything to eat or drink.		
8.	Reports and documents incident.		

Date Reviewed ____________ Instructor Signature ____________

Date Performed ____________ Instructor Signature ____________

Responding to a myocardial infarction			
		yes	no
1.	Calls for help immediately.		
2.	Places person in a comfortable position. Encourages him to rest, and reassures him that he will not be left alone.		

		yes	no
3.	Loosens clothing around the neck.		
4.	Does not give person liquids or food.		
5.	Monitors person's breathing and pulse. Begins CPR if breathing and pulse are absent.		
6.	Stays with person until help arrives.		
7.	Reports and documents incident.		

_____   _____
Date Reviewed   Instructor Signature

_____   _____
Date Performed   Instructor Signature

Controlling bleeding

		yes	no
1.	Calls for help immediately.		
2.	Puts on gloves.		
3.	Holds clean towel, cloth, or handkerchief against the wound.		
4.	Presses down hard directly on the bleeding wound until help arrives. Does not decrease pressure. Puts additional towel over the first towel if blood seeps through. Does not remove the first towel.		
5.	Raises the wound above level of the heart to slow bleeding.		
6.	When bleeding is under control, secures dressing to keep it in place. Checks person for symptoms of shock. Stays with person until help arrives.		
7.	Removes and discards gloves. Washes hands.		
8.	Reports and documents incident.		

_____   _____
Date Reviewed   Instructor Signature

_____   _____
Date Performed   Instructor Signature

Treating burns

		yes	no
	Minor burns:		
1.	Puts on gloves.		
2.	Uses cool, clean water (not ice or ice water) to decrease the skin temperature and prevent further injury. Does not use ointment, salve, or grease. Dampens a clean cloth with cool water and covers burn.		
3.	Covers area with a dry, clean dressing or non-adhesive sterile bandage.		
4.	Removes and discards gloves. Washes hands.		
5.	Reports and documents incident.		
	Serious burns:		
1.	Removes person from the source of burn.		
2.	Calls for help immediately. Puts on gloves.		
3.	Checks for breathing, pulse, and severe bleeding. Begins CPR if breathing and pulse are absent. Does not apply ointment, water, salve, or grease.		
4.	Does not remove clothing from burned areas. Covers burn with sterile gauze or a clean sheet without rubbing skin.		
5.	Monitors vital signs and waits for emergency medical help.		
6.	Removes and discards gloves. Washes hands.		
7.	Reports and documents incident.		

_____   _____
Date Reviewed   Instructor Signature

_____   _____
Date Performed   Instructor Signature

Name: _____

Responding to seizures

		yes	no
1.	Notes the time. Puts on gloves.		
2.	Lowers person to the floor.		
3.	Has someone call emergency medical help. Does not leave person unless has to get medical help.		
4.	Moves furniture away to prevent injury.		
5.	Does not try to restrain the person or stop the seizure.		
6.	Does not force anything between the person's teeth. Does not place hands in person's mouth.		
7.	Does not give food or fluids.		
8.	When the seizure is over, notes time. Turns person to left side if head, neck, back, spinal, or abdominal injuries are not suspected. Checks breathing and pulse. Begins CPR if breathing and pulse are absent.		
9.	Removes and discards gloves. Washes hands.		
10.	Reports and documents incident.		

_____ Date Reviewed _____ Instructor Signature

_____ Date Performed _____ Instructor Signature

Responding to fainting

		yes	no
1.	Has person lie down or sit down before fainting occurs.		
2.	If person is sitting, has him bend forward (he can place his head between his knees if able). If person is lying flat on his back, elevates his legs about 12 inches.		
3.	Loosens any tight clothing.		
4.	Has person stay in position for at least five minutes after symptoms disappear.		
5.	Helps person get up slowly. Continues to observe him for symptoms of fainting.		
6.	If person does faint, lowers him to floor, positioning him on his back. Elevates legs 8 to 12 inches if no head, neck, back, spinal, or abdominal injuries are suspected. Contacts supervisor.		
7.	Reports and documents incident.		

_____ Date Reviewed _____ Instructor Signature

_____ Date Performed _____ Instructor Signature

Responding to a nosebleed

		yes	no
1.	Elevates head of the bed or tells client to remain in sitting position, leaning forward. Offers tissues or a clean cloth.		
2.	Puts on gloves. Applies firm pressure on both sides of the nose, near the bridge. Squeezes sides with thumb and forefinger.		
3.	Applies pressure consistently until bleeding stops.		
4.	Uses a cool cloth or ice wrapped in a cloth on bridge of nose to slow blood flow.		
5.	Removes and discards gloves. Washes hands.		
6.	Reports and documents incident.		

_____ Date Reviewed _____ Instructor Signature

_____ Date Performed _____ Instructor Signature

	Helping a client who has fallen	yes	no
1.	Assesses client's condition and gets help if condition warrants it.		
2.	Looks for broken bones.		
3.	Asks client to move each body part separately to observe.		
	If sprain or fracture is suspected:		
4.	Calls supervisor and reports fall.		
	Keeps injured area in one position. Does not move client.		
	Keeps client covered with blanket.		
	If no injury is suspected:		
	Makes the client comfortable.		
	Calls supervisor and reports fall.		
	Does not move client until talked with supervisor.		
5.	Reports and documents incident.		

_____ _____
Date Reviewed   Instructor Signature

_____ _____
Date Performed   Instructor Signature

9
Body Systems and Related Conditions

	Providing foot care for the client with diabetes	yes	no
1.	Washes hands.		
2.	Explains procedure to client, speaking clearly, slowly, and directly. Maintains face-to-face contact whenever possible.		
3.	Provides privacy.		
4.	Fills the basin halfway with warm water. Tests water temperature and has client check water temperature. Adjusts if necessary.		

		yes	no
5.	Places basin on bath mat or towel in comfortable position for client. Supports foot and ankle throughout.		
6.	Puts on gloves.		
7.	Removes socks and submerges feet. Soaks for 10 to 20 minutes.		
8.	Washes feet one at a time, with washcloth and soap, and rinses in warm water. Rinses the feet.		
9.	Pats the feet dry, wiping between the toes.		
10.	Gently rubs lotion into the feet with circular strokes. Does not put lotion between the toes.		
11.	Observes the skin for signs of dryness, irritation, etc.		
12.	Helps client put on socks and shoes or slippers.		
13.	Disposes of used linens. Cleans and stores basin and supplies.		
14.	Removes and discards gloves.		
15.	Washes hands.		
16.	Documents procedure and any observations.		

_____ _____
Date Reviewed   Instructor Signature

_____ _____
Date Performed   Instructor Signature

12
Positioning, Transfers, and Ambulation

	Moving a client up in bed	yes	no
	If client cannot assist:		
1.	Washes hands.		
2.	Explains procedure to client, speaking clearly, slowly, and directly. Maintains face-to-face contact whenever possible.		
3.	Provides privacy.		
4.	Adjusts the bed to safe working level. Locks bed wheels.		

Name: _____

5.	Lowers head of bed. Moves pillow to head of bed.		
6.	Stands behind head of bed with feet apart and one foot slightly in front of other.		
7.	Rolls and grasps top of draw sheet. Bends knees, keeping back straight, and rocks weight from front foot to back foot, while pulling client toward head of bed.		
8.	Positions client comfortably, arranges pillow and blankets, unrolls draw sheet, and returns bed to lowest position.		
9.	Washes hands.		
10.	Documents procedure and any observations.		

_____   _____
Date Reviewed   Instructor Signature

_____   _____
Date Reviewed   Instructor Signature

	When you have help from another person:		
1.	Washes hands.		
2.	Explains procedure to client, speaking clearly, slowly, and directly. Maintains face-to-face contact whenever possible.		
3.	Provides privacy.		
4.	Adjusts the bed to safe working level. Locks bed wheels.		
5.	Lowers head of bed. Moves pillow to head of bed.		
6.	Stands on opposite side of bed from helper. Turns slightly toward the head of bed, points foot closest toward head of bed.		
7.	Rolls and grasps top of draw sheet with palms up at client's shoulders and hips.		

8.	Shifts weight to back foot and on count of three, both workers shift weight to forward feet while sliding draw sheet toward head of bed.		
9.	Positions client comfortably, arranges pillow and blankets, unrolls draw sheet, and returns bed to lowest position.		
10.	Washes hands.		
11.	Documents procedure and any observations.		

_____   _____
Date Reviewed   Instructor Signature

_____   _____
Date Performed   Instructor Signature

Moving a client to the side of the bed			
		yes	no
1.	Washes hands.		
2.	Explains procedure to client, speaking clearly, slowly, and directly. Maintains face-to-face contact whenever possible.		
3.	Provides privacy.		
4.	Adjusts the bed to safe working level. Locks bed wheels. Lowers head of bed.		
5.	Stands on same side of bed to where client will be moved.		
6.	*With a draw sheet:* Rolls draw sheet up and grasps draw sheet with palms up. Puts hand at client's shoulders, and the other at client's hips. Applies one knee against side of bed, leans back, and pulls draw sheet and client toward self on the count of three.		
	Without a draw sheet: Slides hands under head and shoulders and moves toward self. Slides hands under midsection and moves toward self. Slides hands under hips and legs and moves toward self.		

Name: _____

7.	Returns bed to lowest position.		
8.	Washes hands.		
9.	Documents procedure and any observations.		

_____ _____
Date Reviewed   Instructor Signature

_____ _____
Date Performed   Instructor Signature

Positioning a client on left side

		yes	no
1.	Washes hands.		
2.	Explains procedure to client, speaking clearly, slowly, and directly. Maintains face-to-face contact whenever possible.		
3.	Provides privacy.		
4.	Adjusts the bed to a safe working level. Locks bed wheels. Lowers head of bed.		
5.	Moves client toward right side of bed. Raises side rail on left side of the bed.		
6.	Crosses client's right arm over chest and moves left arm out of the way. Crosses right leg over left leg.		
7.	Stands with feet apart and knees bent. Places one hand on client's right shoulder and the other hand on the client's right hip.		
8.	Gently rolls client onto his left side as one unit, toward the raised side rail. If bed does not have a side rail, rolls client toward self.		
9.	Positions client properly and comfortably, using pillows or other supports.		
10.	Returns bed to lowest position.		
11.	Washes hands.		

12.	Documents procedure and any observations.		

_____ _____
Date Reviewed   Instructor Signature

_____ _____
Date Performed   Instructor Signature

Logrolling a client

		yes	no
1.	Washes hands.		
2.	Explains procedure to client, speaking clearly, slowly, and directly. Maintains face-to-face contact whenever possible.		
3.	Provides privacy.		
4.	Adjusts the bed to safe working level. Locks bed wheels. Lowers head of bed.		
5.	Both workers stand on same side of bed, one at the client's head and shoulders, one near the midsection.		
6.	Places pillow under the client's head. Places client's arm across his chest and places pillow between the knees.		
7.	Stands with feet about shoulder-width apart, bends knees, and grasps draw sheet on far side.		
8.	Rolls client toward self on count of three, turning client as a unit.		
9.	Positions client comfortably with pillows or supports, and checks for proper alignment. Returns bed to lowest position.		
10.	Washes hands.		
11.	Documents procedure and any observations.		

_____ _____
Date Reviewed   Instructor Signature

_____ _____
Date Performed   Instructor Signature

Assisting a client to sit up on side of bed: dangling		yes	no
1.	Washes hands.		
2.	Explains procedure to client, speaking clearly, slowly, and directly. Maintains face-to-face contact whenever possible.		
3.	Provides privacy.		
4.	Adjusts the bed to lowest position. Locks bed wheels.		
5.	Raises head of bed to sitting position. Fanfolds top covers to foot of bed and assists client to turn onto side, facing self.		
6.	Has client reach across chest with top arm and place hand on edge of bed near opposite shoulder. Asks client to push down on that hand while swinging legs over the side of bed.		
7.	If client needs assistance, stands with legs shoulder-width apart and bends knees.		
8.	Places one arm under client's shoulder blades and the other under his thighs.		
9.	Turns client into sitting position on count of three.		
10.	With client holding onto edge of mattress, puts nonskid shoes on client. Does not leave client alone.		
11.	Returns client safely to bed or completes walking or transfer according to care plan. Returns bed to lowest position.		
12.	Washes hands.		
13.	Documents procedure and any observations.		

_____   _____
Date Reviewed   Instructor Signature

_____   _____
Date Performed   Instructor Signature

Transferring a client from bed to wheelchair		yes	no
1.	Washes hands.		
2.	Explains procedure to client, speaking clearly, slowly, and directly. Maintains face-to-face contact whenever possible.		
3.	Provides privacy.		
4.	Places wheelchair at the head of the bed, facing the foot of the bed, or at the foot of bed, facing the head of bed. Wheelchair should be on client's stronger side. Removes footrests. Locks wheelchair wheels.		
5.	Raises head of bed and adjusts bed level to lowest position. Locks bed wheels.		
6.	Assists client to sitting position with feet flat on floor. Puts non-skid shoes on client and fastens.		
7.	Stands in front of client with feet about shoulder-width apart. Bends knees. Places transfer belt around client's waist over clothing and grasps belt on both sides with hands in upward position.		
8.	Provides instructions to assist with transfer. Braces client's lower legs. Helps client stand on count of three.		
9.	Instructs client to take small steps to the chair while turning his back toward chair. Helps client to pivot to front of chair if necessary.		
10.	Asks client to put hands on chair armrests and helps client to lower himself into the chair.		
11.	Attaches footrests and places client's feet on them. Positions client in the chair properly and removes transfer belt. Places robe over lap.		
12.	Washes hands.		

Name: _____

13.	Documents procedure and any observations.		

_____ _____
Date Reviewed   Instructor Signature

_____ _____
Date Performed   Instructor Signature

Helping a client transfer using a slide board		yes	no
1.	Washes hands.		
2.	Explains procedure to client, speaking clearly, slowly, and directly. Maintains face-to-face contact whenever possible.		
3.	Provides privacy.		
4.	Places wheelchair at the head of the bed, facing the foot of the bed, or at the foot of bed, facing the head of bed. Wheelchair should be on client's stronger side. Removes footrests. Locks wheelchair wheels.		
5.	Raises head of bed and adjusts bed level to lowest position. Locks bed wheels.		
6.	Assists client to sitting position with feet flat on floor. Puts non-skid shoes on client and fastens.		
7.	Has client lean away from the transfer side.		
8.	Places one end of slide board under client's buttocks and thigh and the other end on the surface to which client is transferring.		
9.	Instructs client to push up with hands and scoot across the board.		
10.	If client needs assistance, braces client's knees, grasps the transfer belt, and instructs client to lean forward. Helps client scoot across the board, without dragging client.		

11.	Removes slide board after transfer is complete. Positions client comfortably and safely.		
12.	Washes hands.		
13.	Documents procedure and any observations.		

_____ _____
Date Reviewed   Instructor Signature

_____ _____
Date Performed   Instructor Signature

Transferring a client using a mechanical lift		yes	no
1.	Washes hands.		
2.	Explains procedure to client, speaking clearly, slowly, and directly. Maintains face-to-face contact whenever possible.		
3.	Provides privacy.		
4.	Locks bed wheels. Positions wheelchair next to bed and locks brakes.		
5.	Positions sling under client.		
6.	Positions mechanical lift next to bed, opening the base to its widest point and pushes base of lift under bed. Positions overhead bar directly over client.		
7.	Attaches straps to sling properly.		
8.	Raises client in sling two inches above bed, following manufacturer's instructions. Pauses to let client gain balance.		
9.	Rolls mechanical lift to position client over chair or wheelchair. Lifting partner supports and guides client's body.		
10.	Slowly lowers client into chair or wheelchair, pushing down gently on client's knees.		
11.	Undoes straps from overhead bar to sling, leaving sling in place.		

Name: _____

12.	Positions client comfortably and correctly.		
13.	Washes hands.		
14.	Documents procedure and any observations.		

_____ _____
Date Reviewed   Instructor Signature

_____ _____
Date Performed   Instructor Signature

10.	Removes gait belt and returns the client to bed or a chair. Positions client comfortably. Leaves bed in lowest position.		
11.	Washes hands.		
12.	Documents procedure and any observations.		

_____ _____
Date Reviewed   Instructor Signature

_____ _____
Date Performed   Instructor Signature

Assisting a client to ambulate

		yes	no
1.	Washes hands.		
2.	Explains procedure to client, speaking clearly, slowly, and directly. Maintains face-to-face contact whenever possible.		
3.	Provides privacy.		
4.	Adjusts the bed to low position so that feet are flat on the floor. Locks bed wheels. Puts nonskid footwear on client.		
5.	Stands in front of and faces client.		
6.	Places belt around client's waist over clothing and grasps belt on both sides with hands in upward position.		
7.	If client needs help, braces client's lower extremities and bends knees. Has client lean forward and push down on bed with hands. Rocks weight onto back foot to assist client to standing position on count of three.		
8.	Walks slightly behind and to one side of client, on weaker side, for distance while holding on to gait belt. Asks client to look forward, not down at feet.		
9.	Observes client's strength and provides chair if client becomes tired.		

Assisting with ambulation for a client using a cane, walker, or crutches

		yes	no
1.	Washes hands.		
2.	Explains procedure to client, speaking clearly, slowly, and directly. Maintains face-to-face contact whenever possible.		
3.	Provides privacy.		
4.	Adjusts the bed to low position so that feet are flat on the floor. Locks bed wheels. Puts nonskid footwear on client.		
5.	Stands in front of and faces client.		
6.	Places gait belt around client's waist over clothing and grasps belt on both sides with hands in upward position.		
7.	Braces client's lower extremities and bends knees. Assists client to stand.		
8.	Helps as needed with ambulation with cane, walker, or crutches, walking slightly behind or on the weak side of client.		
9.	Watches for obstacles in the client's path. Asks client to look forward, not down at feet.		
10.	Lets the client set the pace, encouraging rest as necessary.		

11.	Removes gait belt. Returns the client to bed or a chair. Positions client comfortably. Leaves bed in lowest position.		
12.	Washes hands.		
13.	Documents procedure and any observations.		

_____   _____
Date Reviewed   Instructor Signature

_____   _____
Date Performed   Instructor Signature

Giving a back rub

		yes	no
1.	Washes hands.		
2.	Explains procedure to client, speaking clearly, slowly, and directly. Maintains face-to-face contact whenever possible.		
3.	Provides privacy.		
4.	Adjusts the bed to safe working level. Lowers head of bed. Locks bed wheels.		
5.	Positions client to lie on side or stomach. Covers client with blanket and folds back bed covers, exposing client's back to the top of the buttocks.		
6.	Warms lotion and hands. Pours lotion onto hands and rubs hands together. Warns client that lotion may still feel cool.		
7.	Starting at the upper part of the buttocks, makes long, smooth upward strokes with both hands. Circles hands up along spine, shoulders, and then back down along the outer edges of the back. Repeats for three to five minutes.		

8.	Starting at the base of the spine, makes kneading motions using the first two fingers and thumb of each hand. Circles hands up along spine, circling at shoulders and buttocks.		
9.	Gently massages bony areas. Massages around any red areas, rather than on them.		
10.	Lets client know when back rub is almost completed.		
11.	Dries the back.		
12.	Removes blanket or towel, assists client with getting dressed, and positions client comfortably. Returns bed to lowest position.		
13.	Stores lotion and puts dirty linens in hamper.		
14.	Washes hands.		
15.	Documents procedure and any observations.		

_____   _____
Date Reviewed   Instructor Signature

_____   _____
Date Performed   Instructor Signature

13
Personal Care Skills

Helping the client transfer to the bathtub

		yes	no
1.	Washes hands.		
2.	Explains procedure to client, speaking clearly, slowly, and directly. Maintains face-to-face contact whenever possible.		
3.	Helps client to the bathroom.		
4.	Provides privacy.		
5.	Seats client in chair facing tub. If using wheelchair, locks brakes, and raises footrests.		
6.	Asks client to place legs one at a time over sides of tub.		

7.	Assists client to sitting position on edge of tub.		
8.	Lowers client into tub properly, assisting as necessary.		
9.	Reverses procedure to help client out of tub.		
10.	Washes hands.		
11.	Documents procedure and any observations.		

Date Reviewed _____ Instructor Signature

Date Performed _____ Instructor Signature

Helping the ambulatory client take a shower or tub bath

		yes	no
1.	Washes hands.		
2.	Explains procedure to client, speaking clearly, slowly, and directly. Maintains face-to-face contact whenever possible.		
3.	Cleans tub or shower if necessary, places mat, and sets up tub or shower chair. Places non-skid rug next to tub.		
4.	Provides privacy.		
5.	Fills tub with warm water (no higher than 105°F on bath thermometer) or adjusts shower water temperature. Has client test water temperature and adjusts as necessary.		
6.	Puts on gloves.		
7.	Assists client to undress and helps client transfer to tub or shower.		
8.	If client is able to bathe alone, places supplies and signal near client. Checks on client every five minutes. If client is weak, stays in bathroom.		
9.	If showering, stays with client and assists.		

10.	Assists client as necessary, washing from clean to dirty areas. Makes sure all soap is rinsed off.		
11.	Assists with shampooing.		
12.	Helps client out and assists client with drying if necessary.		
13.	Helps client get dressed and back to bed.		
14.	Cleans tub. Places soiled laundry in laundry hamper.		
15.	Removes and discards gloves.		
16.	Washes hands.		
17.	Stores supplies.		
18.	Documents procedure and any observations.		

Date Reviewed _____ Instructor Signature

Date Performed _____ Instructor Signature

Giving a complete bed bath

		yes	no
1.	Washes hands.		
2.	Explains procedure to client, speaking clearly, slowly, and directly. Maintains face-to-face contact whenever possible.		
3.	Provides privacy.		
4.	Makes sure room is comfortable temperature. Adjusts the bed to a safe working level. Locks bed wheels.		
5.	Asks client to remove glasses and jewelry. Offers bedpan.		
6.	Places blanket over client and removes or folds back top bedding.		
7.	Fills basin and checks temperature (no higher than 105°F on bath thermometer). Has client test water temperature and adjusts if necessary.		
8.	Puts on gloves.		

9.	Asks and assists client to participate in washing.		
10.	Uncovers only one part of the body at a time. Places a towel under the body part being washed.		
11.	Washes, rinses, and dries one part of the body at a time. Starts at the head, works down, and completes front first. Uses a clean area of the washcloth for each stroke.		
	Eyes, Face, Ears, and Neck: Washes face with wet washcloth (no soap). Begins with the eyes, and washes inner area to outer area, using a different area of the washcloth for each eye. Washes the face from the middle outward using firm but gentle strokes. Washes ears and behind the ears and washes neck. Rinses and pats dry.		
	Arms and Axillae: Washes upper arm and underarm. Uses long strokes from the shoulder down to the wrist. Rinses and pats dry. Repeats for other arm.		
	Hands: Washes hand in a basin. Cleans under nails. Rinses and pats dry. Gives nail care. Repeats for other hand. Applies lotion.		
	Chest: Lifts the towel only enough to wash the chest, rinse it, and pat dry. For a female client: washes, rinses, and dries breasts and under breasts.		
	Abdomen: Folds blanket down so that it still covers pubic area. Washes abdomen, rinses, and pats dry.		
	Legs and Feet: Exposes one leg and places towel under it. Washes thighs. Uses long downward strokes. Rinses and pats dry. Does the same from the knee to the ankle.		

	Places towel under foot and washes foot and between the toes in a basin. Rinses foot and pats dry, making sure area between toes is dry. Gives nail care if it has been assigned. Applies lotion if ordered but not between the toes. Repeats for other leg and foot.		
	Back: Helps client move to the center of the bed, then turns client onto his side so back is facing self. Washes neck and back with long, downward strokes. Rinses and pats dry. Applies lotion if ordered.		
12.	Places towel under buttocks. Helps client turn onto back. Removes and discards gloves. Washes hands and puts on clean gloves before washing perineal area.		
13.	**Perineal area and buttocks:** Changes bath water. Washes, rinses, and dries perineal area, working from front to back.		

	For a female client: Washes the perineum with small amount of soap and water from front to back, using single strokes. Uses a clean area of washcloth or clean washcloth for each stroke. Wipes one side of the labia majora. Then wipes the other side, using a clean part of the cloth. Spreads the labia majora and wipes from front to back on one side. Then wipes from front to back on the other side. Wipes from front to back in the center. Cleans the perineum last with a front to back motion. Rinses the area thoroughly in the same way, making sure all soap is removed. Dries entire perineal area moving from front to back, using a blotting motion with towel. Asks client to turn on her side. Washes, rinses, and dries buttocks and anal area. Cleans anal area without contaminating the perineal area.		
	For a male client: If client is uncircumcised, pulls back the foreskin first. Gently pushes skin towards the base of penis. Holds the penis by the shaft and washes in a circular motion from the tip down to the base. Uses a clean area of washcloth or clean washcloth for each stroke. Rinses the penis. If client is uncircumcised, gently returns foreskin to normal position. Then washes the scrotum and groin. Rinses and pats dry. Asks client to turn on his side. Washes, rinses, and dries buttocks and anal area. Cleans anal area without contaminating the perineal area.		

14.	Covers client. Places soiled washcloths and towels in proper container. Rinses and dries basin. Removes and discards gloves.		
15.	Washes hands.		
16.	Gives back rub if time permits.		
17.	Assists client with grooming as necessary. Returns bed to lowest position.		
18.	Stores everything. Dons clean gloves if bed sheets and blankets need to be changed.		
19.	Washes hands.		
20.	Documents procedure and any observations.		

_____   _____
Date Reviewed   Instructor Signature

_____   _____
Date Performed   Instructor Signature

Shampooing hair

		yes	no
1.	Washes hands.		
2.	Explains procedure to client, speaking clearly, slowly, and directly. Maintains face-to-face contact whenever possible.		
3.	Provides privacy. Makes sure that room is comfortable temperature.		
4.	Checks water temperature (no higher than 105°F). Has client test water temperature and adjusts if necessary.		
5.	Positions client in sink, tub, shower, or bed, and wets hair.		
6.	Applies shampoo, and massages scalp with fingertips (not fingernails).		
7.	Rinses hair thoroughly. Repeats.		
8.	Wraps client's hair in towel.		
9.	Removes towel and combs/ brushes hair.		
10.	Dries and styles hair.		

11.	Washes and stores equipment. Places soiled washcloths and towels in proper container. Returns bed to lowest position.		
12.	Washes hands.		
13.	Documents procedure and any observations.		

_____   _____
Date Reviewed   Instructor Signature

_____   _____
Date Performed   Instructor Signature

12.	Discards water and cleans basin. Disposes of towels in proper place and stores supplies. Returns bed to lowest position. Removes and discards gloves.		
13.	Washes hands.		
14.	Documents procedure and any observations.		

_____   _____
Date Reviewed   Instructor Signature

_____   _____
Date Performed   Instructor Signature

Providing fingernail care

		yes	no
1.	Washes hands.		
2.	Explains procedure to client, speaking clearly, slowly, and directly. Maintains face-to-face contact whenever possible.		
3.	Provides privacy.		
4.	Adjusts bed to a safe working level. Locks bed wheels.		
5.	Removes rings and nail polish if necessary.		
6.	Fills basin with warm water (no higher than 105°F). Has client test water temperature and adjusts if necessary.		
7.	Puts on gloves.		
8.	Soaks hands and nails for at least five minutes.		
9.	Removes hands from water. Washes hands with soapy washcloth. Rinses. Dries client's hands with a towel, including between fingers. Removes basin.		
10.	Cleans under nails with orangewood stick. Wipes orangewood stick on towel after each nail. Washes the hands again and dries, including between fingers.		
11.	Shapes fingernails with an emery board or nail file. Finishes with nails smooth and free of rough edges. Applies lotion.		

Providing foot care

		yes	no
1.	Washes hands.		
2.	Explains procedure to client, speaking clearly, slowly, and directly. Maintains face-to-face contact whenever possible.		
3.	Provides privacy.		
4.	Fills basin with warm water (no higher than 105°F). Has client test water temperature and adjusts if necessary.		
5.	Places basin on a bath mat or bath towel on the floor or on a towel at the foot of the bed.		
6.	Puts on gloves.		
7.	Soaks client's feet for 10 to 20 minutes, adding warm water as necessary.		
8.	Removes one foot from water. Washes entire foot, including between the toes and around nail beds with soapy washcloth.		
9.	Rinses and dries entire foot, including between the toes.		
10.	Repeats steps for other foot.		
11.	Applies lotion (except between toes).		
12.	Helps client put on socks.		

13.	Discards water and cleans basin. Disposes of towels and stores supplies. Returns bed to lowest position. Removes and discards gloves.		
14.	Washes hands.		
15.	Documents procedure and any observations.		

_____   _____
Date Reviewed   Instructor Signature

_____   _____
Date Performed   Instructor Signature

8.	Puts towel and linens in hamper. Returns bed to lowest position. Cleans and stores equipment.		
9.	Removes and discards gloves. Washes hands.		
10.	Documents procedure and any observations.		

_____   _____
Date Reviewed   Instructor Signature

_____   _____
Date Performed   Instructor Signature

Shaving a client

		yes	no
1.	Washes hands.		
2.	Explains procedure to client, speaking clearly, slowly, and directly. Maintains face-to-face contact whenever possible.		
3.	Provides privacy.		
4.	Places equipment within reach. Adjusts bed to a safe working level. Locks bed wheels. Places towel across client's chest.		
5.	Puts on gloves.		
6.	*If using a safety or disposable razor,* softens beard, lathers face, holds skin taut, and shaves in direction of hair growth. Rinses blade often. Rinses and dries face. Offers mirror.		
	If using an electric razor, turns it on, holds skin taut, and shaves with smooth, even movements. Shaves back and forth in direction of beard growth with foil shaver. Shaves in circular motion with three-head shaver. Shaves the chin and under the chin. Offers mirror.		
7.	Applies aftershave lotion if client desires.		

Combing or brushing hair

		yes	no
1.	Washes hands.		
2.	Explains procedure to client, speaking clearly, slowly, and directly. Maintains face-to-face contact whenever possible.		
3.	Provides privacy.		
4.	If in bed, raises head of bed. Adjusts bed to a safe working level. Locks bed wheels. If ambulatory, provides a chair. Places towel under head or around shoulders.		
5.	Removes hair pins, hair ties, or clips.		
6.	If hair is tangled, detangles gently.		
7.	Brushes hair properly.		
8.	Styles hair in the way the client prefers. Offers a mirror to client.		
9.	Removes towel, and places linen in hamper. Cleans and stores supplies. Returns bed to lowest position.		
10.	Washes hands.		
11.	Documents procedure and any observations.		

_____   _____
Date Reviewed   Instructor Signature

_____   _____
Date Performed   Instructor Signature

156

Dressing a client

		yes	no
1.	Washes hands.		
2.	Explains procedure to client, speaking clearly, slowly, and directly. Maintains face-to-face contact whenever possible.		
3.	Provides privacy.		
4.	Asks what client would like to wear and dresses her in outfit of choice.		
5.	Removes gown or top, taking clothes off stronger side first, then weaker side. Places gown in hamper.		
6.	Helps put weaker arm through sleeve of top, then stronger side.		
7.	Helps put on skirt, pants, or dress, putting weaker leg through pants first, then stronger leg.		
8.	Locks bed wheels and places bed in lowest position. After client is sitting, puts on socks and nonskid shoes and fastens shoes.		
9.	Finishes with client dressed appropriately, with zippers and buttons fastened. Places worn clothing in hamper. Leaves bed in lowest position.		
10.	Washes hands.		
11.	Documents procedure and any observations.		

Date Reviewed _____ Instructor Signature _____

Date Performed _____ Instructor Signature _____

2.	Explains procedure to client, speaking clearly, slowly, and directly. Maintains face-to-face contact whenever possible.		
3.	Provides privacy.		
4.	If client is in bed, helps him into upright sitting position. Adjusts bed to a safe working level. Locks bed wheels.		
5.	Puts on gloves. Places towel under head and across chest.		
6.	Removes dental bridgework.		
7.	Wets brush and puts a small amount of toothpaste on brush.		
8.	Gently brushes teeth, including tongue and all surfaces of teeth and gumline. First brushes inner, outer, and chewing surfaces of the upper teeth, then does the same with the lower teeth. Brushes tongue.		
9.	Assists client to rinse mouth and to spit into emesis basin.		
10.	Wipes client's mouth and removes towel.		
11.	Replaces dental bridgework. Applies moisturizer to lips.		
12.	Rinses toothbrush and stores it. Discards water, and washes and stores basin. Puts towels in hamper and stores supplies. Returns bed to lowest position.		
13.	Removes and discards gloves. Washes hands.		
14.	Documents procedure and any observations.		

Date Reviewed _____ Instructor Signature _____

Date Performed _____ Instructor Signature _____

Providing oral care

		yes	no
1.	Washes hands.		

Providing oral care for the unconscious client

		yes	no
1.	Washes hands.		

Name: _____

2.	Explains procedure to client, speaking clearly, slowly, and directly. Maintains face-to-face contact whenever possible.		
3.	Provides privacy.		
4.	Adjusts bed to a safe working level. Locks bed wheels.		
5.	Puts on gloves.		
6.	Turns client's head to side and places a towel under cheek and chin. Places basin next to cheek and chin.		
7.	Holds mouth open with tongue depressor. Dips swab in solution and squeezes swab to remove excess solution. Wipes inner, outer, and chewing surfaces of upper and lower teeth, gums, tongue, and inside surfaces of mouth. Changes swab often. Repeats until clean.		
8.	Rinses with clean swab.		
9.	Removes towel and basin. Applies moisturizer to lips.		
10.	Discards water, and washes and stores basin. Puts towels in hamper and stores supplies. Returns bed to lowest position.		
11.	Removes and discards gloves. Washes hands.		
12.	Documents procedure and any observations.		

_____ _____
Date Reviewed   Instructor Signature

_____ _____
Date Performed   Instructor Signature

Flossing teeth

		yes	no
1.	Washes hands.		
2.	Explains procedure to client, speaking clearly, slowly, and directly. Maintains face-to-face contact whenever possible.		

3.	Provides privacy.		
4.	Helps client get into upright sitting position. Adjusts bed to safe working level. Locks bed wheels.		
5.	Puts on gloves.		
6.	Wraps floss around fingers.		
7.	Flosses teeth, starting with the back teeth.		
8.	Uses clean area of floss after every two teeth.		
9.	Offers water periodically and offers a towel when done.		
10.	Discards water, and washes and stores basin. Puts towels in hamper and stores supplies. Returns bed to lowest position.		
11.	Removes and discards gloves. Washes hands.		
12.	Documents procedure and any observations.		

_____ _____
Date Reviewed   Instructor Signature

_____ _____
Date Performed   Instructor Signature

Cleaning and storing dentures

		yes	no
1.	Washes hands.		
2.	Explains procedure to client, speaking clearly, slowly, and directly. Maintains face-to-face contact whenever possible.		
3.	Provides privacy.		
4.	Puts on gloves.		
5.	Lines sink or basin with towel and partially fills with water.		
6.	Removes lower denture properly if client is unable.		
7.	Removes upper denture properly.		

Name: _____

8.	Rinses dentures in clean moderate/cool running water. Applies denture cleanser to toothbrush and brushes all surfaces. Rinses all surfaces under moderate/cool running water.		
9.	Rinses denture cup and places dentures in it.		
10.	If client prefers, soaks dentures in solution.		
11.	Stores dentures in water or solution in labeled denture cup, or returns dentures to client.		
12.	Rinses toothbrush and stores it. Washes and stores supplies.		
13.	Removes and discards gloves. Washes hands.		
14.	Documents procedure and any observations.		

_____   _____
Date Reviewed   Instructor Signature

_____   _____
Date Performed   Instructor Signature

Reinserting dentures

		yes	no
1.	Washes hands.		
2.	Explains procedure to client, speaking clearly, slowly, and directly. Maintains face-to-face contact whenever possible.		
3.	Provides privacy.		
4.	Positions client in upright position.		
5.	Puts on gloves.		
6.	Applies denture cream.		
7.	Inserts upper denture at an angle, pressing it firmly onto upper gum line.		
8.	Inserts lower denture, pressing it firmly onto the lower gum line.		
9.	Offers client face towel.		

10.	Rinses and stores denture cup. Places towel in hamper and stores supplies.		
11.	Removes and discards gloves. Washes hands.		
12.	Documents procedure and any observations.		

_____   _____
Date Reviewed   Instructor Signature

_____   _____
Date Performed   Instructor Signature

Assisting a client with use of a bedpan

		yes	no
1.	Washes hands.		
2.	Explains procedure to client, speaking clearly, slowly, and directly. Maintains face-to-face contact whenever possible.		
3.	Provides privacy.		
4.	Adjusts bed to a safe working level. Lowers head of bed. Locks bed wheels.		
5.	Puts on gloves.		
6.	Warms outside of bedpan with warm water.		
7.	Covers client with bath blanket and places a bed protector under client.		
8.	Asks client to remove undergarments or helps client to do so.		
9.	Places bedpan near hips. Positions standard bedpan with wider end aligned with the buttocks. Positions fracture pan with handle toward foot of bed. Slides bedpan under hips.		
10.	Removes and discards gloves. Washes hands. Raises head of bed after placing bedpan.		
11.	Provides client with supplies. Asks client to clean his hands after bedpan use. Leaves room and closes door until client calls.		

Name: _____

12.	When called, returns and washes hands. Puts on clean gloves. Lowers head of bed. Removes and covers bedpan. If client is unable, gives perineal care.		
13.	Covers client and removes bath blanket. Discards soiled supplies. Places linens in hamper.		
14.	Takes bedpan to the bathroom. Notes contents before flushing. Empties bedpan into toilet. Rinses bedpan with cold water and empties. Flushes toilet. Cleans bedpan with hot, soapy water and stores.		
15.	Removes and discards gloves.		
16.	Washes hands. Returns bed to lowest position.		
17.	Documents procedure and any observations.		

_____ _____
Date Reviewed   Instructor Signature

_____ _____
Date Performed   Instructor Signature

Assisting a male client with a urinal

		yes	no
1.	Washes hands.		
2.	Explains procedure to client, speaking clearly, slowly, and directly. Maintains face-to-face contact whenever possible.		
3.	Provides privacy.		
4.	Adjusts the bed to a safe working level. Locks bed wheels.		
5.	Puts on gloves.		
6.	Places bed protector under client's buttocks and hips.		
7.	Hands urinal to client or places it if client is unable. Replaces covers.		
8.	Removes and discards gloves. Washes hands. Gives client a bell. Leaves room and closes door until client calls.		

9.	When called, returns and washes hands. Puts on clean gloves. Removes and discards supplies. Removes urinal and empties contents into toilet.		
10.	Takes urinal to the bathroom. Notes contents before flushing. Rinses urinal, flushes toilet, and stores urinal.		
11.	Removes and discards gloves. Washes hands.		
12.	Returns bed to lowest position.		
13.	Documents procedure and any observations.		

_____ _____
Date Reviewed   Instructor Signature

_____ _____
Date Performed   Instructor Signature

Helping a client use a portable commode or toilet

		yes	no
1.	Washes hands.		
2.	Explains procedure to client, speaking clearly, slowly, and directly. Maintains face-to-face contact whenever possible.		
3.	Provides privacy.		
4.	Locks commode wheels. Adjusts the bed to lowest position. Locks bed wheels. Makes sure client is wearing nonskid shoes and helps client to bathroom or commode.		
5.	Puts on gloves.		
6.	Helps client sit. Provides client with supplies and asks client to clean his hands. Removes and discards gloves. Washes hands. Leaves room and closes door until client calls.		
7.	When called, returns and washes hands. Puts on clean gloves. Gives perineal care if help is needed. Discards soiled supplies.		

		yes	no
8.	Removes and discards gloves. Washes hands.		
9.	Helps client back to bed and puts on clean gloves.		
10.	Removes waste container and notes contents. Empties into toilet.		
11.	Cleans container, rinsing first with cold water, then hot, soapy water.		
12.	Removes and discards gloves.		
13.	Washes hands.		
14.	Documents procedure and any observations.		

_____   _____
Date Reviewed   Instructor Signature

_____   _____
Date Performed   Instructor Signature

14
Core Healthcare Skills

Measuring and recording an oral temperature			
		yes	no
1.	Washes hands.		
2.	Explains procedure to client, speaking clearly, slowly, and directly. Maintains face-to-face contact whenever possible.		
3.	Provides privacy.		
4.	Puts on gloves.		
5.	*Mercury-free thermometer:* Holds thermometer by stem. Shakes thermometer down to below the lowest number. *Digital thermometer:* Puts on disposable sheath. Turns on thermometer and waits until ready sign appears. *Electronic thermometer:* Removes probe from base unit and puts on probe cover.		
6.	*Mercury-free thermometer:* Puts on disposable sheath if available. Inserts bulb end of thermometer into client's mouth, under tongue and to one side. *Digital thermometer:* Inserts end of digital thermometer into client's mouth, under tongue and to one side. *Electronic thermometer:* Inserts end of electronic thermometer into client's mouth, under tongue and to one side.		
7.	*For all thermometers:* Asks client to hold thermometer in his mouth with his lips closed and assists as necessary. *Mercury-free thermometer:* Leaves thermometer in place for at least three minutes. *Digital thermometer:* Leaves in place until thermometer blinks or beeps. *Electronic thermometer:* Leaves in place until tone or light signals temperature has been read.		
8.	*Mercury-free thermometer:* Removes thermometer. Wipes with tissue from stem to bulb or removes sheath. Discards tissue or sheath. Reads temperature and remembers reading. *Digital thermometer:* Removes thermometer. Reads temperature on display screen and remembers reading. *Electronic thermometer:* Reads temperature on display screen and remembers reading. Removes probe.		

9.	Mercury-free thermometer: Cleans thermometer with soap and water. Rinses, dries, and stores thermometer. Digital thermometer: Removes and disposes of sheath with a tissue. Stores thermometer. Electronic thermometer: Presses the eject button to discard the cover. Returns probe to holder.		
10.	Removes and discards gloves.		
11.	Washes hands.		
12.	Documents temperature, date, time, and method used (oral).		

_____   _____
Date Reviewed   Instructor Signature

_____   _____
Date Performed   Instructor Signature

Measuring and recording a rectal temperature		yes	no
1.	Washes hands.		
2.	Explains procedure to client, speaking clearly, slowly, and directly. Maintains face-to-face contact whenever possible.		
3.	Provides privacy.		
4.	Adjusts bed to a safe working level. Locks bed wheels. Assists client to left-lying position.		
5.	Folds back linens to only expose rectal area.		
6.	Puts on gloves.		
7.	Mercury-free thermometer: Holds thermometer by stem. Shakes thermometer down to below the lowest number. Digital thermometer: Puts on disposable sheath. Turns on thermometer and waits until ready sign appears. Electronic thermometer: Removes probe from base unit and puts on probe cover.		
8.	Applies a small amount of lubricant to tip of bulb or probe cover.		
9.	Separates buttocks. Gently inserts thermometer into rectum 1/2 to 1 inch. Replaces sheet over buttocks. Holds onto thermometer at all times while taking temperature.		
10.	Mercury-free thermometer: Holds thermometer in place for at least three minutes. Digital thermometer: Holds thermometer in place until thermometer blinks or beeps. Electronic thermometer: Leaves in place until tone or light signals temperature has been read.		
11.	Removes thermometer and wipes thermometer with tissue from stem to bulb or removes sheath. Discards tissue or sheath.		
12.	Reads temperature and remembers reading.		
13.	Mercury-free thermometer: Cleans thermometer with soap and water. Rinses, dries, and stores thermometer. Digital thermometer: Cleans and stores thermometer. Electronic thermometer: Presses the eject button to discard the cover. Returns probe to holder.		
14.	Returns bed to lowest position.		
15.	Removes and discards gloves. Washes hands.		
16.	Documents temperature, date, time, and method used (rectal).		

_____   _____
Date Reviewed   Instructor Signature

_____   _____
Date Performed   Instructor Signature

Name: _____

Measuring and recording a tympanic temperature

		yes	no
1.	Washes hands.		
2.	Explains procedure to client, speaking clearly, slowly, and directly. Maintains face-to-face contact whenever possible.		
3.	Provides privacy.		
4.	Puts on gloves.		
5.	Places disposable sheath over earpiece of thermometer.		
6.	Positions client's head properly and gently pulls up and back on the outside edge of the ear. Inserts covered probe and presses the button.		
7.	Holds thermometer in place until it blinks or beeps.		
8.	Reads temperature and remembers reading.		
9.	Discards sheath and stores thermometer properly.		
10.	Removes and discards gloves.		
11.	Washes hands.		
12.	Documents temperature, date, time, and method used (tympanic).		

_____   _____
Date Reviewed   Instructor Signature

_____   _____
Date Performed   Instructor Signature

Measuring and recording an axillary temperature

		yes	no
1.	Washes hands.		
2.	Explains procedure to client, speaking clearly, slowly, and directly. Maintains face-to-face contact whenever possible.		
3.	Provides privacy.		

4.	Adjusts bed to a safe working level. Lowers head of bed. Locks bed wheels.		
5.	Puts on gloves.		
6.	Removes client's arm from clothing and wipes axillary area with tissues.		
7.	**Mercury-free thermometer:** Holds thermometer by stem. Shakes thermometer down to below the lowest number. **Digital thermometer:** Puts on disposable sheath. Turns on thermometer and waits until ready sign appears. **Electronic thermometer:** Removes probe from base unit and puts on probe cover.		
8.	Positions thermometer in center of armpit and folds client's arm over chest.		
9.	**Mercury-free thermometer:** Holds thermometer in place for 8 to 10 minutes. **Digital thermometer:** Leaves in place until thermometer blinks or beeps. **Electronic thermometer:** Leaves in place until tone or light signals temperature has been read.		
10.	**Mercury-free thermometer:** Removes thermometer. Wipes with tissue from stem to bulb or removes sheath. Discards tissue or sheath. Reads temperature and remembers reading. **Digital thermometer:** Removes thermometer. Reads temperature on display screen and remembers reading. **Electronic thermometer:** Reads temperature on display screen and remembers reading. Removes probe.		

11.	**Mercury-free thermometer:** Cleans thermometer with soap and water. Rinses, dries, and stores thermometer. **Digital thermometer:** Removes and disposes of sheath with a tissue. Stores thermometer. **Electronic thermometer:** Presses the eject button to discard the cover. Returns probe to holder.		
12.	Returns bed to lowest position.		
13.	Removes and discards gloves. Washes hands.		
14.	Documents temperature, date, time, and method used (axillary).		

_____   _____
Date Reviewed   Instructor Signature

_____   _____
Date Performed   Instructor Signature

Counting and recording apical pulse

		yes	no
1.	Washes hands.		
2.	Explains procedure to client, speaking clearly, slowly, and directly. Maintains face-to-face contact whenever possible.		
3.	Provides privacy.		
4.	Before using stethoscope, wipes diaphragm and earpieces with alcohol wipes. Fits earpieces of stethoscope snugly in ears and places flat metal diaphragm on left side of chest, just below the nipple.		
5.	Counts heartbeats for one full minute.		
6.	Counts client's respirations with stethoscope still in place.		
7.	Washes hands.		
8.	Documents pulse rate, date, time, and method used (apical). Notes any irregularities in rhythm.		
9.	Cleans and stores stethoscope.		

10.	Washes hands.		

_____   _____
Date Reviewed   Instructor Signature

_____   _____
Date Performed   Instructor Signature

Counting and recording radial pulse and counting and recording respirations

		yes	no
1.	Washes hands.		
2.	Explains procedure to client, speaking clearly, slowly, and directly. Maintains face-to-face contact whenever possible.		
3.	Provides privacy.		
4.	Places fingertips of index finger and middle finger on the thumb side of client's wrist to locate radial pulse.		
5.	Counts beats for one full minute.		
6.	Keeping fingertips on client's wrist, counts respirations for one full minute.		
7.	Washes hands.		
8.	Documents pulse rate, date, time, and method used (radial). Documents respiratory rate and the pattern or character of breathing.		

_____   _____
Date Reviewed   Instructor Signature

_____   _____
Date Performed   Instructor Signature

Measuring and recording blood pressure (one-step method)

		yes	no
1.	Washes hands.		
2.	Explains procedure to client, speaking clearly, slowly, and directly. Maintains face-to-face contact whenever possible.		
3.	Provides privacy.		

Name: _____

4.	Wipes diaphragm and earpieces of stethoscope with alcohol wipes.		
5.	Asks client to roll up sleeve. Positions client's arm with palm up. The arm should be level with the heart.		
6.	With the valve open, squeezes the cuff to make sure it is completely deflated.		
7.	Places blood pressure cuff snugly on client's upper arm, with the center of the cuff placed over the brachial artery.		
8.	Locates the brachial pulse with fingertips.		
9.	Places earpieces of stethoscope in ears and places diaphragm of stethoscope over brachial artery.		
10.	Closes the valve (clockwise) until it stops. Inflates cuff to between 160 mm Hg to 180 mm Hg. If a beat is heard immediately upon cuff deflation, completely deflates cuff. Reinflates cuff to no more than 200 mm Hg.		
11.	Opens the valve slightly with thumb and index finger. Deflates cuff slowly.		
12.	Watches gauge and listens for sound of pulse.		
13.	Remembers the reading at which the first clear pulse sound is heard. This is the systolic pressure.		
14.	Continues listening for a change or muffling of pulse sound. The point of a change or the point the sound disappears is the diastolic pressure. Remembers this reading.		
15.	Opens the valve to deflate cuff completely. Removes cuff.		
16.	Washes hands.		
17.	Documents both systolic and diastolic pressures. Notes which arm was used.		

18.	Cleans stethoscope. Stores equipment.		
19.	Washes hands.		

_____   _____
Date Reviewed   Instructor Signature

_____   _____
Date Performed   Instructor Signature

Measuring and recording weight of an ambulatory client

		yes	no
1.	Washes hands.		
2.	Explains procedure to client, speaking clearly, slowly, and directly. Maintains face-to-face contact whenever possible.		
3.	Provides privacy.		
4.	Sets scale on hard floor surface. Makes sure client is wearing nonskid shoes.		
5.	Starts with scale at zero.		
6.	Helps client to step on scale as necessary. Makes sure client is not holding, touching, or leaning against anything.		
7.	Determines client's weight. If using a bathroom scale, reads weight on display screen or when dial has stopped moving. If using a standing scale, balances the bar and adds numbers together.		
8.	Helps client to step off the scale and back to a comfortable position.		
9.	Washes hands.		
10.	Documents the weight.		
11.	Stores the scale.		
12.	Washes hands.		

_____   _____
Date Reviewed   Instructor Signature

_____   _____
Date Performed   Instructor Signature

Measuring and recording height of a client			
		yes	no
1.	Washes hands.		
2.	Explains procedure to client, speaking clearly, slowly, and directly. Maintains face-to-face contact whenever possible.		
3.	Provides privacy.		
4.	Positions client straight in bed, flat on the back, with arms and legs at sides. Makes sure bed sheet is smooth underneath client.		
5.	Makes a small pencil mark at the top of client's head and at client's heel.		
6.	Measures distance between the two marks with a tape measure.		
7.	Washes hands.		
8.	Documents client's height.		
9.	Stores equipment.		
10.	Washes hands.		
	For clients who can get out of bed:		
1.	Washes hands.		
2.	Explains procedure to client, speaking clearly, slowly, and directly. Maintains face-to-face contact whenever possible.		
3.	Provides privacy.		
4.	Instructs client to remove shoes and stand with his back against a wall and arms at his sides.		
5.	Makes a small pencil mark on the wall even with the top of the client's head.		
6.	Instructs client to step away. Measures the distance between the pencil mark and the floor.		
7.	Washes hands.		
8.	Documents height.		
9.	Stores equipment.		
10.	Washes hands.		

If using a standing scale:			
1.	Washes hands.		
2.	Explains procedure to client, speaking clearly, slowly, and directly. Maintains face-to-face contact whenever possible.		
3.	Provides privacy.		
4.	Makes sure client has on non-skid shoes and helps client to step onto scale, facing away from the scale.		
5.	With client standing straight, pulls up measuring rod and lowers it until it rests flat on client's head.		
6.	Determines client's height. Assists client to step off the scale and back to a comfortable position.		
7.	Washes hands.		
8.	Documents the height.		

_____   _____
Date Reviewed   Instructor Signature

_____   _____
Date Performed   Instructor Signature

Collecting a sputum specimen			
		yes	no
1.	Washes hands.		
2.	Explains procedure to client, speaking clearly, slowly, and directly. Maintains face-to-face contact whenever possible.		
3.	Provides privacy.		
4.	Puts on mask and gloves.		
5.	Gives client tissues to cover the mouth. Instructs client to cough deeply and spit the sputum into the specimen container.		
6.	Covers container tightly, and wipes any sputum off the outside of the container. Puts container in clean specimen bag and seals bag.		

Name: _____

7.	Removes and discards gloves and mask.		
8.	Washes hands.		
9.	Documents procedure and any observations.		

_____ . _____
Date Reviewed   Instructor Signature

_____   _____
Date Performed   Instructor Signature

10.	Discards tongue blades. Empties and rinses bedpan or container and flushes toilet. Cleans and stores equipment.		
11.	Stores the specimen properly.		
12.	Removes and discards gloves.		
13.	Washes hands.		
14.	Documents procedure and any observations.		

_____   _____
Date Reviewed   Instructor Signature

_____   _____
Date Performed   Instructor Signature

Collecting a stool specimen

		yes	no
1.	Washes hands.		
2.	Explains procedure to client, speaking clearly, slowly, and directly. Maintains face-to-face contact whenever possible.		
3.	Provides privacy.		
4.	Puts on gloves.		
5.	Asks client not to urinate at the same time as moving bowels and not to put toilet paper in with the sample. Provides plastic bag to discard toilet paper separately.		
6.	Fits hat to toilet or provides client with bedpan. Provides client with supplies. Asks the client to call when he is finished.		
7.	Removes and discards gloves. Washes hands. Leaves the room and closes the door.		
8.	When called, returns and washes hands. Puts on clean gloves. Helps with perineal care if needed.		
9.	Uses tongue blades to take about two tablespoons of stool and puts it in container without touching the inside. Covers container tightly, applies label, and places in clean specimen bag.		

Collecting a routine urine specimen

		yes	no
1.	Washes hands.		
2.	Explains procedure to client, speaking clearly, slowly, and directly. Maintains face-to-face contact whenever possible.		
3.	Provides privacy.		
4.	Puts on gloves.		
5.	Fits hat to toilet or provides client with bedpan or urinal. Asks client not to put toilet paper in with the sample. Provides plastic bag to discard toilet paper separately.		
6.	Provides client with supplies. Asks the client to call when he is finished.		
7.	Removes and discards gloves. Washes hands. Leaves the room and closes the door.		
8.	When called, returns and washes hands. Puts on clean gloves. Helps with perineal care if needed.		
9.	Takes bedpan, urinal, or commode pail to the bathroom. Pours urine into specimen container, filling it at least halfway.		

10.	Covers container with lid. Wipes off the outside with a paper towel.		
11.	Applies label and places the container in a clean specimen bag.		
12.	Discards extra urine, rinses container, and flushes toilet. Cleans and stores equipment.		
13.	Removes and discards gloves.		
14.	Washes hands.		
15.	Documents procedure and any observations.		

Date Reviewed   Instructor Signature

Date Performed   Instructor Signature

10.	Covers urine container and wipes off outside with paper towel. Places in a clean specimen bag.		
11.	Discards extra urine, rinses container, and flushes toilet. Cleans and stores equipment.		
12.	Removes and discards gloves.		
13.	Washes hands.		
14.	Documents procedure and any observations.		

Date Reviewed   Instructor Signature

Date Performed   Instructor Signature

Collecting a clean-catch (mid-stream) urine specimen

		yes	no
1.	Washes hands.		
2.	Explains procedure to client, speaking clearly, slowly, and directly. Maintains face-to-face contact whenever possible.		
3.	Provides privacy.		
4.	Puts on gloves.		
5.	Opens specimen kit.		
6.	Cleans perineal area.		
7.	Asks client to urinate into the bedpan, urinal, or toilet and to stop before urination is complete.		
8.	Places container under the urine stream and instructs client to start urinating again until container is at least half full. Has client finish urinating in bedpan, toilet, or urinal.		
9.	Gives perineal care if help is needed and asks client to clean hands.		

Collecting a 24-hour urine specimen

		yes	no
1.	Washes hands.		
2.	Explains procedure to client, speaking clearly, slowly, and directly. Maintains face-to-face contact whenever possible.		
3.	Provides privacy.		
4.	Instructs client to completely empty the bladder. Discards urine and notes the exact time.		
5.	Washes hands and puts on gloves each time client voids.		
6.	Pours urine from bedpan, urinal, or hat into container, using the funnel as needed.		
7.	Assists client with perineal care and to wash hands after each voiding.		
8.	Instructs client and family to save all urine and store properly after each voiding.		
9.	Cleans equipment after each voiding.		
10.	Removes and discards gloves.		
11.	Washes hands.		

Name: _____

12.	Documents procedure and any observations.		

_____	_____
Date Reviewed	Instructor Signature

_____	_____
Date Performed	Instructor Signature

8.	Washes hands.		
9.	Documents the time and amount (in mL) of urine.		

_____	_____
Date Reviewed	Instructor Signature

_____	_____
Date Performed	Instructor Signature

Measuring and recording intake and output

		yes	no
	For measuring intake:		
1.	Washes hands.		
2.	Explains procedure to client, speaking clearly, slowly, and directly. Maintains face-to-face contact whenever possible.		
3.	Provides privacy.		
4.	Measures amount of fluid client is served and notes on paper.		
5.	Measures leftover fluids and notes on paper.		
6.	Subtracts amount left over from amount served. Converts to milliliters (mL).		
7.	Documents amount of fluids consumed (in mL), time, and type of fluid in visit notes or I&O sheet.		
8.	Washes hands.		
	For measuring output:		
1.	Washes hands.		
2.	Explains procedure to client, speaking clearly, slowly, and directly. Maintains face-to-face contact whenever possible.		
3.	Provides privacy.		
4.	Puts on gloves.		
5.	Pours urine into measuring container. Measures amount of urine at eye level and notes amount on paper.		
6.	Discards urine. Washes and stores equipment.		
7.	Removes and discards gloves.		

Observing, reporting, and documenting emesis

		yes	no
1.	Puts on gloves.		
2.	Provides a basin and removes it when vomiting has stopped.		
3.	Removes soiled linens or clothes and replaces with fresh ones.		
4.	Measures and notes amount of vomitus if monitoring client's I&O.		
5.	Discards vomit in toilet unless vomit is red, has blood in it, or looks like wet coffee grounds. Washes and stores basin.		
6.	Removes and discards gloves.		
7.	Washes hands.		
8.	Puts on clean gloves.		
9.	Provides comfort to client.		
10.	Launders soiled linens and clothes in hot water.		
11.	Removes and discards gloves.		
12.	Washes hands.		
13.	Documents time, amount, color, and consistency of vomitus.		
14.	Reports to supervisor immediately.		

_____	_____
Date Reviewed	Instructor Signature

_____	_____
Date Performed	Instructor Signature

Providing catheter care

		yes	no
1.	Washes hands.		

2.	Explains procedure to client, speaking clearly, slowly, and directly. Maintains face-to-face contact whenever possible.		
3.	Provides privacy.		
4.	Adjusts the bed to safe working level. Locks bed wheels. Lowers head of bed and positions client lying flat on back.		
5.	Removes or folds back top bedding, keeping client covered with bath blanket.		
6.	Checks water temperature (no higher than 105°F). Has client test water temperature and adjusts if necessary.		
7.	Puts on gloves.		
8.	Places clean bed protector under client's buttocks.		
9.	Exposes only the area necessary to clean the catheter.		
10.	Places towel or pad under catheter tubing before washing.		
11.	Applies soap to washcloth and cleans area around meatus, using a clean area of the cloth for each stroke.		
12.	Holding catheter near meatus, cleans at least four inches of catheter. Moves in only one direction, away from meatus. Uses a clean area of the cloth for each stroke.		
13.	Dips clean washcloth in water and rinses area around meatus, using a clean area of washcloth for each stroke.		
14.	Dips clean washcloth in water and rinses at least four inches of catheter nearest meatus, moving away from meatus. Uses a clean area of washcloth for each stroke.		

15.	Removes bed protector and towel. Empties water into toilet and flushes. Places linen in proper containers. Cleans and stores basin.		
16.	Removes and discards gloves.		
17.	Washes hands.		
18.	Removes bath blanket and replaces top covers. Returns bed to lowest position.		
19.	Helps client dress. Arranges covers. Checks that catheter tubing is free from kinks and twists and that it is securely taped to the leg.		
20.	Washes hands.		
21.	Documents procedure and any observations.		

_____   _____
Date Reviewed   Instructor Signature

_____   _____
Date Performed   Instructor Signature

Emptying the catheter drainage bag			
		yes	no
1.	Washes hands.		
2.	Explains procedure to client, speaking clearly, slowly, and directly. Maintains face-to-face contact whenever possible.		
3.	Puts on gloves.		
4.	Places measuring container on paper towel on floor under drainage bag.		
5.	Opens clamp on bag so urine flows into graduate.		
6.	Closes clamp and cleans drain spout. Replaces drain spout in its holder on the bag.		
7.	Goes into bathroom. Places graduate on a flat surface and measures at eye level. Notes amount and appearance of urine and empties it into toilet. Flushes toilet.		

Name: _____

8.	Cleans and stores graduate.		
9.	Removes and discards gloves.		
10.	Washes hands.		
11.	Documents procedure and any observations.		

_____   _____
Date Reviewed   Instructor Signature

_____   _____
Date Performed   Instructor Signature

Changing a condom catheter

		yes	no
1.	Washes hands.		
2.	Explains procedure to client, speaking clearly, slowly, and directly. Maintains face-to-face contact whenever possible.		
3.	Provides privacy.		
4.	Adjusts the bed to a safe working level. Locks bed wheels. Lowers head of bed and positions client lying flat on his back.		
5.	Removes or folds back bedding, keeping client covered with bath blanket.		
6.	Puts on gloves.		
7.	Places a clean bed protector under client's buttocks. Adjusts bath blanket to only expose genital area.		
8.	Removes condom catheter if one is in place.		
9.	Assists as necessary with perineal care.		
10.	Moves pubic hair away from penis. Places condom on penis and rolls towards base of penis, leaving space between drainage tip and glans of penis to prevent irritation.		
11.	Secures condom to penis with special tape applied in spiral manner.		

12.	Connects catheter tip to drainage tubing. Makes sure tubing is not twisted or kinked.		
13.	Removes and discards bed protector. Discards used supplies in plastic bag. Places soiled linen in proper container. Cleans and stores supplies.		
14.	Removes and discards gloves.		
15.	Washes hands.		
16.	Removes bath blanket and replaces top covers. Returns bed to its lowest position. Washes hands.		
17.	Documents procedure and any observations.		

_____   _____
Date Reviewed   Instructor Signature

_____   _____
Date Performed   Instructor Signature

Applying warm compresses

		yes	no
1.	Washes hands.		
2.	Explains procedure to client, speaking clearly, slowly, and directly. Maintains face-to-face contact whenever possible.		
3.	Provides privacy.		
4.	Fills basin with warm water (no higher than 105°F). Has client check water temperature and adjusts if necessary.		
5.	Soaks washcloth, wrings it out, and applies to area needing compress. Covers with plastic wrap and towel.		
6.	Notes the time. Checks area every five minutes. Changes compress if cooling occurs.		
7.	Removes compress after 20 minutes, or if area is red, numb, or client complains of pain or discomfort.		

8.	Discards plastic wrap and empties basin in toilet. Cleans and stores basin and other supplies. Puts laundry in hamper.		
9.	Washes hands.		
10.	Documents time, length, and site of procedure and any observations.		

_____ _____
Date Reviewed   Instructor Signature

_____ _____
Date Performed   Instructor Signature

10.	Drains tub or empties basin in toilet. Cleans and stores basin and other supplies. Puts laundry in hamper.		
11.	Washes hands.		
12.	Documents time, length, and site of procedure and any observations. Reports client's response and observations about skin.		

_____ _____
Date Reviewed   Instructor Signature

_____ _____
Date Performed   Instructor Signature

Administering warm soaks

		yes	no
1.	Washes hands.		
2.	Explains procedure to client, speaking clearly, slowly, and directly. Maintains face-to-face contact whenever possible.		
3.	Provides privacy.		
4.	Fills the basin with warm water (no higher than 105°F). Has client check water temperature and adjusts if necessary.		
5.	Places basin on a disposable absorbent pad at a comfortable position for the client. Immerses body part in water, padding the edge of the basin as necessary. Covers client for extra warmth if needed.		
6.	Checks water temperature every five minutes, adding hot water as needed.		
7.	Observes area for redness and discontinues soak if client complains of pain or discomfort.		
8.	Soaks for 15 to 20 minutes or as ordered in the care plan.		
9.	Removes basin or helps client out of the tub. Dries the client.		

Using a hot water bottle

		yes	no
1.	Washes hands.		
2.	Explains procedure to client, speaking clearly, slowly, and directly. Maintains face-to-face contact whenever possible.		
3.	Provides privacy.		
4.	Fills bottle halfway with warm water (no higher than 105°F for adults), presses out excess air, and seals bottle.		
5.	Dries the bottle and checks for leaks. Covers bottle with cloth or towel.		
6.	Applies bottle to the area. Checks skin every five minutes for redness or pain. Adds cold water to bottle if skin is red or client complains of pain.		
7.	Removes bottle after 20 minutes or as ordered in the care plan.		
8.	Empties bottle and washes and stores supplies.		
9.	Washes hands.		

10.	Documents time, length, and site of procedure, and any observations.		

_____   _____
Date Reviewed   Instructor Signature

_____   _____
Date Performed   Instructor Signature

Assisting with a sitz bath

		yes	no
1.	Washes hands.		
2.	Explains procedure to client, speaking clearly, slowly, and directly. Maintains face-to-face contact whenever possible.		
3.	Provides privacy.		
4.	Puts on gloves.		
5.	Fills sitz bath two-thirds full with hot water (no higher than 105°F).		
6.	Places sitz bath on toilet seat and helps client undress and sit down on sitz bath.		
7.	Leaves the room and checks on client every five minutes for weakness or dizziness. Stays with client who is unsteady.		
8.	Assists client out of sitz bath after 20 minutes. Provides towels and helps with dressing as needed.		
9.	Cleans and stores supplies. Puts laundry in hamper		
10.	Removes and discards gloves.		
11.	Washes hands.		
12.	Documents procedure, including the time started and ended, the client's response, and the water temperature.		

_____   _____
Date Reviewed   Instructor Signature

_____   _____
Date Performed   Instructor Signature

Applying ice packs

		yes	no
1.	Washes hands.		
2.	Explains procedure to client, speaking clearly, slowly, and directly. Maintains face-to-face contact whenever possible.		
3.	Provides privacy.		
4.	Fills plastic bag with ice and removes excess air. Covers bag with towel.		
5.	Applies bag to the area as ordered. Uses another towel to cover bag if it is too cold.		
6.	Notes the time and checks the area after five minutes for blisters, or pale, white, or gray skin. Stops treatment if client complains of numbness or pain.		
7.	Removes ice after 20 minutes or as ordered in the care plan. Returns ice bag to freezer. Puts laundry in hamper.		
8.	Washes hands.		
9.	Documents the time, length, and site of procedure. Reports the client's response and any observations about the skin.		

_____   _____
Date Reviewed   Instructor Signature

_____   _____
Date Performed   Instructor Signature

Applying cold compresses

		yes	no
1.	Washes hands.		
2.	Explains procedure to client, speaking clearly, slowly, and directly. Maintains face-to-face contact whenever possible.		
3.	Provides privacy.		
4.	Places bed protector under area, rinses washcloth in basin, and wrings out washcloth.		

5.	Covers the area with towel and applies cold washcloth to the area. Changes washcloths to keep area cold.		
6.	Checks the area after five minutes for blisters, or pale, white, or gray skin. Stops treatment if client complains of numbness or pain.		
7.	Removes compresses after 20 minutes or as ordered in the care plan. Gives client towels as needed to dry the area.		
8.	Empties, cleans and stores basin. Puts laundry in hamper.		
9.	Washes hands.		
10.	Documents the time, length, and site of procedure. Reports the client's response and any observations about the skin.		

_____   _____
Date Reviewed   Instructor Signature

_____   _____
Date Performed   Instructor Signature

7.	Removes and discards gloves in the waste bag. Washes hands.		
8.	Puts on clean gloves.		
9.	Applies clean gauze to wound. Tapes gauze in place.		
10.	Discards supplies.		
11.	Removes and discards gloves.		
12.	Washes hands.		
13.	Documents procedure and any observations.		

_____   _____
Date Reviewed   Instructor Signature

_____   _____
Date Performed   Instructor Signature

Changing a dry dressing using non-sterile technique

		yes	no
1.	Washes hands.		
2.	Explains procedure to client, speaking clearly, slowly, and directly. Maintains face-to-face contact whenever possible.		
3.	Provides privacy.		
4.	Cuts pieces of tape long enough to secure the dressing and hangs tape within reach. Opens gauze package without touching the gauze.		
5.	Puts on gloves.		
6.	Removes soiled dressing gently, observing dressing for odor or drainage. Notes color and size of the wound. Discards used dressing in the waste bag.		

Putting elastic stockings on client

		yes	no
1.	Washes hands.		
2.	Explains procedure to client, speaking clearly, slowly, and directly. Maintains face-to-face contact whenever possible.		
3.	Provides privacy.		
4.	With client lying down in supine position, removes socks, shoes, or slippers, and exposes one leg.		
5.	Turns stocking inside-out at least to heel area.		
6.	Gently places the foot of the stocking over toes, foot, and heel. Makes sure heel is in right place.		
7.	Gently pulls top of stocking over foot, heel, and leg.		
8.	Makes sure that there are no twists and wrinkles in the stocking after it is applied. Makes sure heel of stocking is over heel of foot.		
9.	Repeats for the other leg.		
10.	Washes hands.		

11.	Documents procedure and any observations.		

Date Reviewed	Instructor Signature

Date Performed	Instructor Signature

Caring for an ostomy			
		yes	no
1.	Washes hands.		
2.	Explains procedure to client, speaking clearly, slowly, and directly. Maintains face-to-face contact whenever possible.		
3.	Provides privacy.		
4.	Adjusts the bed to a safe working level. Locks bed wheels.		
5.	Puts on gloves.		
6.	Places bed protector under client. Covers client with a bath blanket and only exposes the ostomy site.		
7.	Removes ostomy pouch carefully. Notes color, odor, consistency, and amount of stool in the pouch.		
8.	Wipes area around the stoma with disposable wipes for ostomy care. Discards wipes in plastic bag.		
9.	Washes area around the stoma using a washcloth and warm soapy water. Moves in one direction, away from the stoma. Pats dry with another towel.		
10.	Places the clean ostomy pouch on client, following instructions. Seals securely. Makes sure the bottom of the pouch is clamped.		
11.	Removes disposable bed protector and discards. Discards plastic bag and places soiled linens in proper containers.		
12.	Removes and discards gloves.		

13.	Washes hands.		
14.	Returns bed to lowest position.		
15.	Documents procedure and any observations.		

Date Reviewed	Instructor Signature

Date Performed	Instructor Signature

15
Medications and Technology in Home Care

Assisting in changing clothes for a client who has an IV			
		yes	no
1.	Washes hands.		
2.	Explains procedure to client, speaking clearly, slowly, and directly. Maintains face-to-face contact whenever possible.		
3.	Provides privacy.		
4.	Adjusts bed to lowest position. Locks bed wheels. Helps client to sitting position with feet flat on the floor.		
5.	Helps client remove the arm without the IV from the clothing.		
6.	Helps client gather clothing on arm with IV site, lifts clothing over IV site, and moves it up the tubing towards the IV bag.		
7.	Lifts IV bag off the pole, keeping it higher than the IV site, slides clothing over IV bag, and replaces IV bag on the pole.		
8.	Sets used clothing aside and gathers the sleeve of the clean clothing.		
9.	Lifts IV bag off the pole again, keeping it higher than the IV site, slides clean clothing over IV bag onto the client's arm, and replaces IV bag on the pole.		

Name: _____

		yes	no
10.	Moves clean clothing over tubing and IV site and onto the client's arm.		
11.	Assists client with putting other arm into clothing.		
12.	Observes the IV for one minute to make sure that it is dripping properly. Checks the tubing and dressing for proper placement.		
13.	Assists client with changing the rest of the clothing.		
14.	Places soiled laundry in laundry hamper and adjusts bed if necessary.		
15.	Washes hands.		
16.	Documents procedure and any observations.		

_____   _____
Date Reviewed   Instructor Signature

_____   _____
Date Performed   Instructor Signature

16
Rehabilitation and Restorative Care

	Assisting with passive range of motion exercises	yes	no
1.	Washes hands.		
2.	Explains procedure to client, speaking clearly, slowly, and directly. Maintains face-to-face contact whenever possible.		
3.	Provides privacy.		
4.	Adjusts the bed to a safe working level. Locks bed wheels.		
5.	Positions client in supine position. Repeats each exercise at least three times.		
	Shoulder: Performs the following movements properly, supporting the client's arm at the elbow and wrist by placing one hand under the elbow and the other hand under the wrist:		

		yes	no
a.	Extension		
b.	Flexion		
c.	Abduction		
d.	Adduction		
	Elbow: Performs the following movements properly, holding the wrist with one hand and holding the elbow with the other:		
a.	Flexion		
b.	Extension		
c.	Pronation		
d.	Supination		
	Wrist: Performs the following movements properly, holding the wrist with one hand and using the fingers of the other hand to help the joint through the motions:		
a.	Flexion		
b.	Dorsiflexion		
c.	Radial flexion		
d.	Ulnar flexion		
	Thumb: Performs the following movements properly:		
a.	Abduction		
b.	Adduction		
c.	Opposition		
d.	Flexion		
e.	Extension		
	Fingers: Performs the following movements properly:		
a.	Flexion		
b.	Extension		
c.	Abduction		
d.	Adduction		
	Hip: Performs the following movements properly, placing one hand under the knee and one under the ankle:		
a.	Abduction		
b.	Adduction		

c.	Internal rotation		
d.	External rotation		
	Knees: Performs the following movements properly, placing one hand under the knee and one under the ankle:		
a.	Flexion		
b.	Extension		
	Ankles: Performs the following movements while properly supporting the foot and ankle:		
a.	Dorsiflexion		
b.	Plantar flexion		
c.	Supination		
d.	Pronation		
	Toes: Performs the following movements properly:		
a.	Flexion		
b.	Extension		
c.	Abduction		
	When all exercises are completed:		
6.	Returns client to comfortable position and covers as appropriate. Returns bed to lowest position.		
7.	Washes hands.		
8.	Documents procedure. Notes any decrease in range of motion or any pain experienced by the client. Notifies supervisor if increased stiffness or physical resistance is noted.		

_____ _____
Date Reviewed   Instructor Signature

_____ _____
Date Performed   Instructor Signature

Assisting with deep breathing exercises

		yes	no
1.	Washes hands.		

2.	Explains procedure to client, speaking clearly, slowly, and directly. Maintains face-to-face contact whenever possible.		
3.	Provides privacy.		
4.	Puts on gown, mask, and goggles as indicated.		
5.	Puts on gloves.		
6.	Has client inhale deeply while sitting up.		
7.	Has client exhale completely.		
8.	Repeats exercise five to ten times.		
9.	Offers tissues or emesis basin as necessary.		
10.	Disposes of tissues and cleans and stores basin.		
11.	Removes gloves, goggles, gown, and mask.		
12.	Washes hands.		
13.	Puts on new gloves.		
14.	Provides mouth care.		
15.	Removes and discards gloves. Washes hands.		
16.	Documents procedure and any observations.		

_____ _____
Date Reviewed   Instructor Signature

_____ _____
Date Performed   Instructor Signature

19
New Mothers, Infants, and Children

Picking up and holding a baby

		yes	no
1.	Washes hands.		
2.	Supports the head at all times when lifting or holding a baby. With the other hand, supports the baby's back and bottom.		
3.	Performs cradle hold properly.		
4.	Performs football hold properly.		

5.	Performs upright hold properly.		

Date Reviewed		Instructor Signature
Date Performed		Instructor Signature

Sterilizing bottles

		yes	no
1.	Washes hands.		
2.	Boils water and puts equipment in.		
3.	Re-boils water for five minutes.		
4.	Removes equipment and discards water. Stores when dry.		

Date Reviewed		Instructor Signature
Date Performed		Instructor Signature

Assisting with bottle feeding

		yes	no
1.	Washes hands.		
2.	Prepares bottle.		
3.	Sits and holds baby properly.		
4.	Inserts bottle nipple, and ensures that baby's head is higher than body.		
5.	Talks or sings to baby during feeding.		
6.	Burps baby, changes diaper, and puts baby down.		
7.	Washes hands.		
8.	Documents procedure and any observations.		
9.	Washes and sterilizes bottle, nipple, and ring.		

Date Reviewed		Instructor Signature
Date Performed		Instructor Signature

Burping a baby

		yes	no
1.	Washes hands.		
2.	Picks up baby, using either of the two safe positions.		
3.	Pats back gently until baby burps.		
4.	Returns baby to safe position.		

Date Reviewed		Instructor Signature
Date Performed		Instructor Signature

Giving an infant sponge bath

		yes	no
1.	Washes hands.		
2.	Puts on gloves.		
3.	Gathers supplies. Fills basin and tests water temperature.		
4.	Holds baby in football hold and washes eyes, then rest of face, using no soap.		
5.	Holds baby in football hold and washes hair.		
6.	Lays baby down, keeping one hand on baby.		
7.	Undresses upper body and washes it. Dries and covers the baby.		
8.	Undresses lower body and washes and dries it.		
9.	Washes perineal area properly.		
10.	Washes bottom and dries completely.		
11.	Applies lotion, keeping baby covered.		
12.	Diapers and dresses baby. Returns baby to safe position.		
13.	Discards water, cleans supplies, and discards gloves.		
14.	Washes hands.		

Name: _____

15.	Documents procedure and any observations.		

_____   _____
Date Reviewed   Instructor Signature

_____   _____
Date Performed   Instructor Signature

Giving an infant tub bath

		yes	no
1.	Washes hands.		
2.	Puts on gloves.		
3.	Gathers supplies. Fills basin and tests water temperature.		
4.	Holds baby in football hold and washes eyes, then rest of face, using no soap.		
5.	Holds baby in football hold and washes hair.		
6.	Lays baby down, undresses, and immerses baby in basin, keeping head above water.		
7.	Uses washcloth to wash from neck down.		
8.	Removes baby from bath and covers immediately.		
9.	Applies lotion, keeping baby covered as much as possible.		
10.	Diapers and dresses baby. Returns baby to safe position.		
11.	Discards water, cleans supplies, and discards gloves.		
12.	Washes hands.		
13.	Documents procedure and any observations.		

_____   _____
Date Reviewed   Instructor Signature

_____   _____
Date Performed   Instructor Signature

Changing cloth or disposable diapers

		yes	no
1.	Washes hands.		

2.	Puts on gloves.		
3.	Undresses baby and removes diaper, keeping one hand on the baby at all times.		
4.	Cleans perineal area.		
5.	Applies ointment as necessary and allows air to circulate.		
6.	Applies cloth or disposable diaper properly.		
7.	Dresses baby and returns to safe position.		
8.	Disposes of diaper properly.		
9.	Removes and discards gloves.		
10.	Washes hands.		
11.	Cleans area and stores supplies.		
12.	Washes hands again.		
13.	Documents procedure and any observations.		

_____   _____
Date Reviewed   Instructor Signature

_____   _____
Date Performed   Instructor Signature

Measuring a baby's weight

		yes	no
1.	Washes hands.		
2.	Places infant scale on firm surface. Places clean paper on scale and starts with scale at zero.		
3.	Undresses baby. Places baby on scale, keeping one hand on baby at all times.		
4.	Reads and remembers weight.		
5.	Removes baby and dresses him. Returns to safe position.		
6.	Washes hands.		
7.	Documents procedure and any observations.		

_____   _____
Date Reviewed   Instructor Signature

_____   _____
Date Performed   Instructor Signature

Measuring a baby's length

		yes	no
1.	Washes hands.		
2.	Prepares firm surface with clean sheet that has markings on it.		
3.	Places baby on surface, keeping one hand on baby at all times.		
4.	Places baby's head at beginning of measured marks. Straightens knee and makes a mark at baby's heel.		
5.	Determines and remembers length.		
6.	Removes baby and returns to safe position.		
7.	Washes hands.		
8.	Documents procedure and any observations.		
	When paper with inch markings is not available:		
1.	Washes hands.		
2.	Prepares firm surface with plain sheet of paper.		
3.	Places baby on surface, keeping one hand on baby at all times.		
4.	Makes pencil mark at top of baby's head. Straightens knee and makes a mark at baby's heel.		
5.	Measures distance with tape measure. Remembers length.		
6.	Washes hands.		
7.	Documents procedure and any observations.		

_____   _____
Date Reviewed   Instructor Signature

_____   _____
Date Performed   Instructor Signature

Taking an infant's axillary, tympanic, or temporal artery temperature

		yes	no
1.	Washes hands.		
2.	Prepares thermometer.		
3.	***For axillary temperature:*** Undresses baby on one side and lays baby down. Places tip of thermometer under the arm. Keeps thermometer in place for three to five minutes or until signal sounds.		
	For tympanic temperature: Lays baby on side. Gently pulls outside of the ear toward back of head. Inserts thermometer tip into ear and presses button. Holds for one second.		
	For temporal artery temperature: Turns on thermometer and places it flat on the forehead. Presses and holds scan button and sweeps thermometer across the forehead, keeping contact with the baby's skin. Releases scan button.		
4.	Removes thermometer and reads temperature, keeping one hand on baby. Dresses baby and returns to safe position.		
5.	Stores thermometer and supplies.		
6.	Washes hands.		
7.	Documents temperature.		

_____   _____
Date Reviewed   Instructor Signature

_____   _____
Date Performed   Instructor Signature

21
Clean, Safe, and Healthy Environments

Cleaning a bathroom

		yes	no
1.	Puts on gloves.		
2.	Wipes all surfaces with disinfectant and sponge or rag.		
3.	Wipes toilet bowl, using different sponge or rag.		

Name: _____

		yes	no
4.	Cleans bathtub, shower, and sink, using a different sponge.		
5.	Scrubs inside of toilet bowl with brush.		
6.	Washes floor.		
7.	Cleans mirror and all glass.		
8.	Places soiled rags in laundry and disposes of waste.		
9.	Stores supplies. Removes and discards gloves.		
10.	Washes hands.		
11.	Documents procedure and any observations.		

_____ _____
Date Reviewed   Instructor Signature

_____ _____
Date Performed   Instructor Signature

Doing the laundry

		yes	no
1.	Sorts clothes carefully, checking pockets and garments.		
2.	Pretreats clothes as necessary.		
3.	Uses correct temperature, laundry products, and washing cycle.		
4.	Dries clothes.		
5.	Hand washes as necessary.		
6.	Folds and hangs clean laundry. Stores clothes.		

_____ _____
Date Reviewed   Instructor Signature

_____ _____
Date Performed   Instructor Signature

Making an occupied bed

		yes	no
1.	Washes hands.		
2.	Explains procedure to client, speaking clearly, slowly, and directly. Maintains face-to-face contact whenever possible.		
3.	Provides privacy.		

		yes	no
4.	Places clean linen on clean surface within reach.		
5.	Adjusts the bed to a safe working level. Locks bed wheels.		
6.	Puts on gloves.		
7.	Loosens top linen from working side and covers client. Removes top sheet.		
8.	Raises side rail on far side of bed and turns client onto her side, toward self and rail.		
9.	Goes to other side of the bed. Loosens bottom soiled linen, mattress pad, and protector on working side.		
10.	Rolls bottom soiled linen toward client, tucking it snugly against the client's back.		
11.	Places and tucks in clean bottom linen, finishing with no wrinkles. Makes hospital corners if necessary.		
12.	Smoothes bottom sheet out toward the client. Rolls extra material toward client and tucks it under client's body.		
13.	Places disposable absorbent pad if using and centers it. Smoothes it out toward client and tucks it under client's body.		
14.	Places draw sheet if using. Smoothes and tucks as with other bedding.		
15.	Raises side rail on working side. Assists client to turn onto clean bottom sheet.		
16.	Goes to other side of bed and lowers side rail. Loosens soiled linen. Rolls linen from head to the foot of bed, avoiding contact with skin or clothes. Places it in a laundry hamper or basket.		

17.	Pulls and tucks in clean bottom linen just like other side, finishing with bottom sheet free of wrinkles.		
18.	Asks client to turn onto her back, keeping client covered. Raises side rail nearest self.		
19.	Unfolds top sheet and places it over client. Slips blanket or old sheet out from underneath. Puts it in the laundry hamper.		
20.	Places a blanket over the top sheet, matching the top edges. Tucks bottom edges of top sheet and blanket under mattress, making square corners on each side. Loosens top linens over client's feet. Folds top sheet over the blanket about six inches.		
21.	Removes pillow and pillowcase. Places pillowcase in the laundry hamper. Removes and discards gloves. Washes hands.		
22.	Places clean pillowcases on pillows. Places them under client's head.		
23.	Returns bed to lowest position. Leaves side rails in ordered position. Carries laundry hamper to laundry area.		
24.	Washes hands.		
25.	Documents procedure and any observations.		

_____   _____
Date Reviewed   Instructor Signature

_____   _____
Date Performed   Instructor Signature

Making an unoccupied bed			
		yes	no
1.	Washes hands.		
2.	Places clean linen on clean surface within reach.		
3.	Adjusts the bed to a safe working level. Locks bed wheels.		

4.	Puts on gloves.		
5.	Loosens soiled linen and rolls it from head to foot of bed. Avoids contact with skin or clothes. Places it in a hamper or basket. Removes pillows and pillowcases and places pillowcases in hamper.		
6.	Removes and discards gloves. Washes hands.		
7.	Remakes bed, spreading mattress pad and bottom sheet, tucking under. Makes hospital corners. Puts on disposable absorbent pad and draw sheet, smoothes, and tucks under sides of bed.		
8.	Places top sheet and blanket, centering them. Tucks under end of bed and makes hospital corners. Folds down top sheet over the blanket about six inches.		
9.	Puts on clean pillowcases. Replaces pillows.		
10.	Returns bed to its lowest position. Carries laundry hamper to laundry area.		
11.	Washes hands.		
12.	Documents procedure and any observations.		

_____   _____
Date Reviewed   Instructor Signature

_____   _____
Date Performed   Instructor Signature

22
Clients' Nutritional Needs

Assisting a client with eating			
		yes	no
1.	Washes hands.		
2.	Explains procedure to client, speaking clearly, slowly, and directly. Maintains face-to-face contact whenever possible.		

3.	Ensures client is in upright sitting position. Adjusts bed height so she is sitting at client's eye level. Locks bed wheels.		
4.	Helps client to wash hands. Helps client to put on clothing protector if desired.		
5.	Sits at client's eye level on stronger side.		
6.	Tells the client what foods are on the plate. Asks what she would like to eat first. Checks temperature of food. Offers food in bite-sized pieces and alternates types of food offered. Makes sure client's mouth is empty before offering the next bite of food or sip of drink.		
7.	Offers drinks throughout the meal. Talks throughout the meal.		
8.	Wipes client's mouth and hands as necessary.		
9.	Removes clothing protector if used. Removes tray or dishes.		
10.	Assists client to a comfortable position, keeping client upright for at least 30 minutes. Returns bed to lowest position.		
11.	Washes hands.		
12.	Documents procedure (including client's intake if required) and any observations.		

Date Reviewed _____ Instructor Signature _____

Date Performed _____ Instructor Signature _____